The HIMS
(Human Intervention Motivation Study)
NIGHTMARE

A Pilot's Guide to Surviving Substance Abuse Re-Education

Randle Patrick McMurphy

Praise for The HIMS Nightmare...

"The HIMS Nightmare *is an indispensable guide for any pilot who must go through the Human Intervention Motivation Study recovery program. It's rich with solid research and facts, lucidly told by someone who's experienced. It's yet another example of the harms caused by a one-size-fits-all treatment policy based entirely on AA."*

—Joe Miller, US of AA: How the Twelve Steps Hijacked the Science of Alcoholism

****

"This shockingly powerful book needs to be read by every pilot flying commercially in the skies today ... a step-by-step manual on how to navigate the mine fields of the horror show HIMS really is. The 'man behind the curtain' is not a health care or mental health professional or a substance abuse PhD, but rather an antiquated, religious self-help group founded in the 1930s."

—Monica Richardson, host of the podcast "Safe Recovery" and producer of *The 13th Step*, a documentary on sexual exploitation in AA.

****

"... a clear-eyed, engaging and darkly funny look at how substance abuse re-education is being applied to place airline pilots under The Corporate Thumb ..."

—Anonymous pilot #1

****

"The HIMS Nightmare *is right on in all respects. It represents nothing less than SERE [Survival, Evasion, Resistance, and Escape] training for pilots shot down over the hostile territory occupied by HIMS."*

—Anonymous Pilot #2

Copyright © 2019 by Bacchus USA Publications, LLC

All rights reserved.

No part of this publication may be reproduced, stored in a retrieval system, or transmitted in any form or by any means, electronic, mechanical, photocopying, recording, scanning, or otherwise, without the prior written permission of the author.

Limit of Liability/Disclaimer of Warranty: While the publisher and author have used their best efforts in preparing this book, they make no representations with respect to the completeness of the contents of this book and specifically disclaim any implied warranties of merchantability or fitness for a particular purpose. No warranty may be created or extended by sales representatives or written sales materials. The advice and strategies contained herein may not be suitable for your situation. You should consult with a professional when appropriate. Neither the publisher nor the author shall be liable for any loss of profit or any other commercial damages, including but not limited to special, incidental, consequential, personal, or other damages.

The HIMS Nightmare:

A Pilot's Guide to Surviving Substance Abuse Re-Education

By Randle Patrick McMurphy

Print ISBN: 978-1-7348824-0-7

E-book ISBN: 978-1-7348824-1-4

LCCN: 2020906908

Bacchus USA Publications, LLC

Post Office Box 599

Bryson City, NC 28713

BacchusUSAPublications.com

Dedication

I drew my inspiration for **The HIMS Nightmare** *(such as it is) from the chief pilots determined to get rid of me; the HIMS overseers who tortured me for being insufficiently supplicant; and, of course, from the inestimable Dr. "Win," without whose efforts my career might still be intact. My first toast will be to them.*

My first dedication goes to my endlessly loving and understanding wife, who held me through the long and anguishing nights of the company's battle to rip out my soul and replace it with that of a happily lobotomized worker bee.

With her support, I won.

They only got my career.

My second dedication goes to Ken Kesey, author of **One Flew Over the Cuckoo's Nest**, *who understood "The threat of extinction and the reduction of a strong human being seems to be part of the work of the elusive 'Combine,' an entity that unifies individuals to further its own corporate interests and a machine that threshes, cuts, and cleans whatever is in its path." He also depicted the conundrum of behavioral patients:*

"Either conform and be released or maintain your integrity and be kept in the ward."*

I voted for integrity.

---

* Robert Faggen, *One Flew Over the Cuckoo's Nest* introduction, Penguin Books, 2003.

About the Author

"...what I do have are a very particular set of skills. Skills I have acquired over a very long career. Skills that make me a nightmare for people like you." – Liam Neeson, "Taken"

Call me "Captain Asshole." Having served as an airline pilot for 33 years, I came into the Human Intervention Motivation Study (HIMS) program from the unique perspective of being, in my "other life," a political activist and writer for more than 25 years. Trained in hard-core grassroots mobilization tactics in the 1990s, I learned to make an art of extracting compliance from governmental bodies and corporations.

Initially overwhelmed by people who wanted to "help" me, I succumbed to the HIMS program. Gradually, however, I realized that the more I adopted the program's demands for powerlessness, gratitude, and surrender to God (a.k.a. your "higher power"), the more miserable I became. It also began to dawn on me that the HIMS program was really about control. Namely, placing as many pilots as possible under the thumb of a cabal of airline management and substance abuse quacks who could end their careers at any time, for any reason.

Then came the fateful day when my chief pilot, using something I said during a HIMS meeting, committed a potential violation of the Americans with Disabilities Act, which is supposed to protect recovering alcoholics as well as those who reject religion. When I had the audacity to speak of the violation at a HIMS monthly monitoring meeting, the retaliation began.

What happened next was straight out of *One Flew Over the Cuckoo's Nest*. I was removed from the line and remanded to the company psychiatrist for "evaluation" (read that "re-education"). Next, when I was deemed insufficiently supplicant, I was kept out of work and remanded to anger management counseling. Finally, when I refused to allow them complete access to every bit of my life in their effort to gather information to get rid of me, the psychiatrist, who made his living by rubber-stamping airline decisions, tried to diagnose me with "narcissistic personality disorder" – a diagnosis he himself described as "potentially career-ending."

Please note that through all of this, I carefully complied with **all** program requirements, including complete abstinence from mood-altering substances, with the intent of giving them no concrete excuse to eject me from the program. But HIMS personnel accustomed to subjects either drinking the Kool-Aid, playing "cooperate to graduate," failing out of the program or, occasionally, committing suicide, were unprepared to deal with someone willing and able to use their every abuse of power against them.

Before the sceptic in you says, "This guy is probably just a malcontent," understand that each and every step I made was with the prior review of lawyers and behavioral health specialists not associated with HIMS, all of whom were appalled at the atrocities to which I was being subjected.

As I write this, the maneuvering continues. But whatever the ultimate financial disposition, I have won by escaping with my personality intact. What follows is my effort to spare you the pain and injury HIMS routinely inflicts on its victims.

Important Change to HIMS Requirements!

As *The HIMS Nightmare* goes to press, the FAA has announced a huge change to HIMS program monitoring requirements. Previously, numerous HIMS victims I interviewed said they were lied to as they were sucked into the program, particularly with respect to abstinence monitoring. Often, they were told that monitoring via random drug testing fourteen times per year, twice monthly group aftercare, thrice weekly attendance of AA meetings, annual psychiatric evaluations, monthly HIMS monitoring meetings, weekly contacts with peer monitors, etc. would only last for three years. In truth, I have yet to encounter a HIMS victim *recently* issued a Special Issuance Medical Certificate (SI) who got less than five years monitoring.

But fear not, because the FAA has "solved" the problem. How, you ask? By forcing *all* HIMS victims to endure *lifetime* monitoring. This will reportedly apply not only to those just receiving a new SI, but also retroactively to everyone who *currently* holds an SI. No exceptions. So in any part of the book where I have referenced three- or five-year monitoring, you may substitute "for the rest of your flying career." And while some lawyers might claim they can get you released from monitoring prior to the end of your SI, in reality reports suggest the FAA rarely approves such releases.

The upside (if such can be said) is that HIMS victims who previously played the game called "cooperate to graduate," regurgitating AA slogans and groveling to their HIMS overseers, are now sufficiently outraged to actually do something about the nightmare to which they are being subjected. Some are hiring lawyers. Others are contemplating career changes.

I am now fielding calls from previously supplicant airline pilots complaining that this is not the "deal" they signed up for. I explain to them that there was no "deal." They signed up for a program in which HIMS bureaucrats and the FAA can change the rules at any time, for any (or no) reason. The SI they so tenuously clutch is a privilege, not a right, and can be revoked at the pleasure of the FAA, HIMS personnel, or their airline. In short, HIMS victims signed up for a never-ending nightmare which will haunt them for the rest of their careers.

As I write this, the FAA has not announced exactly what lifetime monitoring will mean. One pilot said his employer speculated it would require him to periodically blow into his "Soberlink®" wireless breathalyzer for the rest of his career. Whether that will be every four hours of his waking existence, as is currently required for Soberlink® monitoring prior to receiving an SI, is anybody's guess. Because each airline independently certifies its own program, lifetime monitoring requirements will probably vary.

But I can say two things with reasonable certainty: First, union HIMS representatives, who are often "steppers" (AA cultists), are unlikely to help. In fact, they might welcome this modern version of indentured servitude. Second, **lifetime monitoring changes none of the advice given in this book**. If anything, it reinforces my advice to, if possible, seek any substance abuse treatment you might feel you need from a professional who has never even heard of the HIMS program.

Welcome to *The HIMS Nightmare.*

HIMS Nightmare:
CONTENTS

**HIMS Nightmare
Introduction / 1**

Chapter 1
The Five Fundamental Understandings of HIMS / 8

Chapter 2
What to Expect From HIMS / 12

Chapter 3
So, You (or Others) Think You Might Be Alcoholic / 30

Chapter 4
The Recovery Industry and You / 39

Chapter 5
AA, HIMS, ...and Death / 53

Chapter 6
Navigating HIMS: Up to Your 'SI' / 63

Chapter 7
Navigating HIMS: Your 'SI' and Beyond / 81

Chapter 8
Substance Testing & Monitoring / 92

Chapter 9
Lawyering Up? / 100

Chapter 10
To HIMS, or Not to HIMS? / 114

Appendix A
Glossary of Terms / 120

Appendix B
DSM-5* Criteria for 'Alcohol Use Disorder' / 124

Appendix C
HIMS Certification Process / 125

Appendix D
HIMS AME Checklist / 126

Appendix E-1
FAA Special Issuance Authorization (SIA) / 127

Appendix E-2
FAA Special Issuance Authorization (SIA) / 128

Appendix E-3
FAA Special Issuance Authorization (SIA) / 129

Appendix E-4
FAA Special Issuance Authorization (SIA) / 130

Appendix E-5
FAA Special Issuance Authorization (SIA) / 131

Appendix F
Resources / 132

Want to connect with fellow HIMS victims?

Might get sucked into the HIMS tornado?

Get survival tips and guidelines, and commiserate with others who share your plight, as well as finding links to career-saving resources:

www.HIMSNightmare.com

HIMS Nightmare
Introduction

The purpose of HIMS is "to establish the pilot is developing healthy recovery-oriented thinking patterns..."
– himsprogram.com[1]

"Power is in tearing human minds to pieces and putting them together again in new shapes of your own choosing."
– George Orwell, *1984*

Had this book existed two years before I wrote it, I might have avoided having my nearly 35-year airline career ripped out from underneath me, forcing me to salvage what I could by enduring the cult-like nightmare known as the "Human Intervention Motivation Study" or HIMS program.

Billed as an expedited means for returning drug and alcohol-abusing pilots to the flight deck, HIMS programs have swept major airlines and are now the cure of choice. Although, as the disclaimer goes, "terms and conditions may vary," all major airlines and many regional carriers have reportedly adopted such programs.

While potentially hopeless substance abusers might need to be in a program like HIMS to shed their habit and save their lives, airlines – particularly those in which pilots are protected from corporate abuse by union contracts – have found in HIMS a goldmine of meekly compliant pilots whom they can keep under their corporate thumbs, and are now busily sucking as many victims as possible into the program.

Whatever the original motivations of the program at its inception in 1974, HIMS now represents an unholy alliance of substance dependence recovery and corporate discipline which neatly sidesteps virtually all of the protections typically afforded employees, particularly those embodied in union contracts. The unspoken but very real message is, "Shut up and take what we give you, or we will end your career." For this, HIMS victims, in a grotesque exercise of "Stockholm Syndrome," are expected to express gratitude.

Effectively blackmailed by the loss of FAA medical certificates necessary for their livelihoods – certificates which become null and void upon the diagnosis of alcohol or drug dependence – thousands of professional airline pilots, including many with no alcohol or drug-related crimes or misdeeds, are being sucked into an ever-growing vortex from which escape is unlikely.

Read this book before enrolling (or being forced to enroll) in the HIMS program. Far from being an "Oh, woe is me!" exercise in the self-pity you are probably feeling, what follows is a practical guide intended to let you know what to expect, what to avoid, what to do if pressured into the program, and how best to survive its seemingly infinite clutches.

Had I but known…

This is the book I sought but could not find when the vortex known as HIMS was sucking me in. Had I but known the true purpose and extent of the program, I would have fought tooth and nail to stay out of it. As you contemplate entering the program, you will be directed to lots of rosy videos of pilots saying how HIMS saved their lives. By contrast, this book shows **both** sides of the coin.

My "nom de plume" derives from something I called myself early on, first at rehab and then at a required monthly meeting between my crew base's many HIMS victims, program bureaucrats and one of the chief pilots. Wallowing in my ostensible recovery, when asked to introduce myself to the group, I fell on the sword to ingratiate myself by describing my undiplomatic pre-rehab persona as "Captain Asshole." Little did I know that in a disciplinary meeting several months later, the attending chief pilot representative would use the words I uttered in confidence against me.

My involvement in HIMS started with a relatively minor argument with a hotel security guard, who promptly reported me to the company. Although my time from hotel bar to flight was well outside both the FAA and company-mandated minimums, the next morning my company performed a fitness evaluation prior to my flight. They found me fit to fly, and I completed the day's flying without incident.

Alas, the story was not over: To justify its overzealous actions, the hotel graciously sent an inaccurate bar bill to my chief pilot who, having long had me in his disciplinary sights due to a union job action, remanded me to the physical exam permitted by our contract. The exam included a PEth test, which purports to measure high chronic alcohol consumption but can actually reflect a single night of drinking. Despite having consumed alcohol only once during the month prior to testing, PEth levels reportedly came in high, the examining psychiatrist ginned up his report to back up the PEth results, and my FAA medical certificate became instantly null and void.

Thus began my own personal HIMS nightmare. Initially, the biggest liars I encountered were my "fellow" pilots[2], the collaborators of HIMS who, even before my medical evaluation, began calling me to encourage that I "seek help" despite knowing nothing about me. The fact that I had no DUIs, had never been arrested for anything, and had both a happy marriage and good relationships with my kids didn't seem to impress them. They were quite determined to "help" me.

Rehab would be a "walk in the park," they said. The program would be a breeze, I would regain my medical in six months, and the monitoring for my Special Issuance Medical Certificate (SI) would last only three years, they insisted. After that, I would be free to do whatever I wished, provided I never again consumed alcohol.

In truth, rehab was an expensive, gut-wrenching hell whose thirty days of utter isolation wreaked havoc on my life. In aftercare and monitoring, I was treated like a prison inmate, and when I finally got my SI (after *nine* months, but still far faster than many pilots), my perfect record of HIMS treatment and compliance entitled me to a mere *five* years of additional monitoring. (Oh, and I was fortunate: Having apparently been a "distinguished graduate" from rehab, I was allowed to skip the intensive outpatient therapy (IOP) which would have mandated driving several hours a day, several days a week, to therapy *in addition* to the 90 Alcoholics Anonymous meetings I was forced to attend in my first 90 days after release from rehab.)

Later, lawyers who deal with HIMS told me that in truth, many (if not most) victims *never* get released from monitoring and are stuck in HIMS for the remainder of their careers. Incidentally, those would be the lawyers I consulted when, after a year of flying the line in perfect compliance with the program, I had the audacity to raise the issue of a probable violation of the Americans With Disabilities Act (which does indeed protect recovering alcoholics) by my chief pilot, after which I was promptly pulled from line flying and subjected to still more re-education. What followed were seemingly endless months of misery-drenched, demoralizing and soul-sucking survival – a fate which I hope *The HIMS Nightmare* will help you avoid.

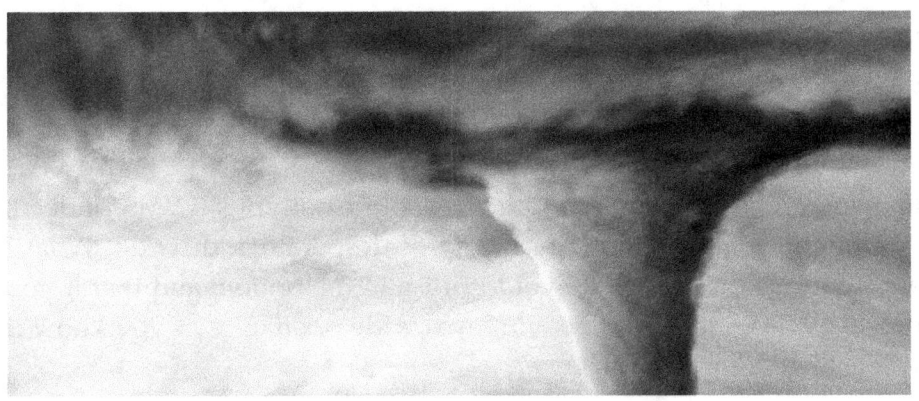

Top 5 reasons you might need this book

(with apologies to David Letterman)

#5: You are any pilot who consumes alcohol within 24 hours of flight.
#4: You might be one of the estimated 12.7% of population who has alcohol addiction "issues" and you fly airplanes.
#3: You are any professional pilot who consumes alcohol or recreational drugs *at all*, <u>**especially if you have had a DUI at any time, even decades ago**</u>.
#2: You are contemplating a career in aviation – especially for an airline – and want to know what the hazards are and how to navigate them. And finally…
#1: The number one reason you need this book:

The HIMS EF5 tornado is bearing down on you, and is about to suck you into its vortex to join thousands of other hapless victims.

HIMS might be your only option…

If you register positive for alcohol or drugs in DOT (Department of Transportation) testing prior or subsequent to flight, HIMS will probably be your only recourse. Ditto for multiple DUIs, a DUI with a blood alcohol concentration (BAC) of 0.15 or higher, or refusing a motor vehicle sobriety test. Even if you bite the bullet and try to restore your medical independently, your airline might not employ you unless you enroll in HIMS.

I'm *not* saying that you absolutely should not enter HIMS; indeed, you might *need* the program. Plenty of desperate addicts do. What I am saying is that *I* would avoid it if I had the option, and that if you do elect HIMS, it should be with eyes wide open. Life as you know it will change.

This book will be roundly denounced

Having just come from what my company describes as an "All Hands" meeting – a company-wide meeting of HIMS administrators, company representatives and approximately 250 HIMS victims, just from my airline – the Kool-Aid-drinking session I just witnessed makes me realize how much some of these people will hate what I have to say. Many in attendance had a hunted look in their eyes. (I picked out several on the hotel bus to the conference.) That look is fear; the fear of loss of control of their lives and of the potential end of their careers, their livelihoods, even their personalities.

To those who fanatically defend HIMS, the views herein are heresy, punishable by the most extreme measures. Their denunciations will dispute my revelations on the true motives of the program and will likely claim I am "killing people" by teaching them how to defend themselves from a HIMS designed to manipulate them. In their eyes, you – as a "drunk" – can't be trusted with this information and must be "protected" from yourself.

Worse, some of the denunciations will come from the pilot collaborators themselves – union representatives to the program and others so thoroughly inculcated into AA and HIMS that they avert their eyes to its officially sanctioned evils, even when those evils conflict with their beliefs. I can assure you that in HIMS, cognitive dissonance is alive and well.

The apologists will ultimately deny the effectiveness of *The HIMS Nightmare*. But since AA and HIMS seem to revolve around slogans, please allow me to offer one of my own. An axiom I have learned in my 25 years of confrontational politics is this: "The more your target denies your effectiveness, the more effective you actually are."

'Institutional conspiracy'

Perhaps the most disturbing thing about HIMS is that its administrators seem to *know* they are violating pilots' rights on a daily basis, including systematic violations of the Americans with Disabilities Act (ADA) and the Health Insurance Portability and Accountability Act (HIPAA). They demonstrate that knowledge by going silent (and then retaliating) when you call them out on violations.

I'm not big on conspiracy theories, but when I recently watched a movie detailing how so many in the hierarchy of the Catholic Church knew but kept quiet about priests abusing children long before it became an issue, a phrase came to mind which neatly describes the HIMS program: "institutional conspiracy." The effectiveness of the HIMS institutional conspiracy rests on keeping pilots isolated and afraid – afraid of losing their careers, their homes, their children's education, and their marriages. My goal is to empower pilots to organize and end that fear-based subjugation.

References:

1. "Recommended Practices: Medical Re-certification," http://www.himsprogram.com/Content/RP_ReCert
2. A notable exception to the "liars" category of pilots who helped administer HIMS was my second peer monitor, a gentleman whom I could always trust to be a straight shooter. I thank him for putting up with me.

Chapter 1
The Five Fundamental Understandings of HIMS

"What do you think you are, for Chrissake, crazy or somethin'? Well you're not! You're not!

You're no crazier than the average asshole out walkin' around on the streets and that's it."
— Randle Patrick McMurphy, *One Flew Over the Cuckoo's Nest*

According to the sages of Alcoholics Anonymous (AA) and HIMS, as a substance abuser you are "insane." As such, you are "powerless" over your life, and most certainly over your drug of choice.

I initially accepted their wisdom ... at least until I gradually began to realize that despite the stated intent of the program, abstinence from alcohol wasn't nearly enough to placate them, and that nothing less than complete supplication would suffice.

The turning point was my re-education session with the shrink, who threatened me with a potentially career-ending diagnosis of "narcissistic personality disorder" unless I not only complied with the program, but embraced the humility being demanded. Feeling a little like McMurphy in the Ken Kesey novel, I asked the shrink: "Doctor, have you ever read *One Flew Over the Cuckoo's Nest*?"

I'm quite certain that, almost imperceptibly, I saw him recoil. That's when I knew I was on to something.

'God, grant me the serenity...'

Perhaps you will consider these fundamental understandings of the HIMS program to be advantageous, even laudable. Perhaps not. But they are facts you must be prepared to accept if you participate in

HIMS. As you will so often hear (and say) in AA, "God, grant me the serenity to accept the things I cannot change..." (or not).

❑ **Understanding #1:** Unlike AA, the primary objective of HIMS is not to relieve your addiction; it is to make you a compliant employee. (Gentle voices will tell you otherwise, of course.) Even though the substance abuse professionals contracted by your employer to administer the program might indeed keep your best interests in mind (at least to the degree they do not conflict with your employer's), make no mistake: The program is not for you, it is for your airline.

❑ **Understanding #2:** Once admitted to HIMS, you have no rights. No right to speak in your own defense, if you are accused of non-compliance; perhaps no right to representation by your union on HIMS-related issues; no right to participate in decisions impacting your future, or even to hear all of the charges against you. In truth, nothing you say would be believed anyway. You are a drunk, and therefore a habitual liar. Your protestations that you did not actually take the drug for which your urinalysis comes back with a false positive will fall on seemingly sympathetic but decidedly deaf ears.

❑ **Understanding #3:** You are on your own. Nobody associated with the program is your ally (especially counselors and psychiatrists, and not even fellow HIMS victims, who may sacrifice you in favor of their "recovery") and, with limited exceptions, nobody outside the program can help you. When you call your union rep to complain about being abused by the company, his or her sympathetic response might well be, "Sorry. I could help you if it was a contractual issue, but we can't do anything about HIMS." Even the lawyers you contact will not be especially encouraging and will say: "Yeah, that is probably a violation of the ADA, but the company will argue that you aren't complying with your recovery program, and it will be up to you to prove otherwise."

- **Understanding #4:** Anything you say can and *will* be used against you. That especially includes the things you tell the nice psychiatrist who insists he is trying to help you but will dutifully report your every utterance as evidence of your alcoholism or mental disorder. That nice psychiatrist is paid by your company; you are not his patient, and he has no legal obligation to treat you, much less protect your most private secrets. Oh, yes: Secrets? You won't have them anymore. At rehab, AA and monitoring meetings, you will be required to divulge your most guarded shame. If you fail to do so, you will be judged as insufficiently sincere in your recovery. Your required stay in rehab may be extended (one pilot I knew in rehab had it extended *twice*), and you may be subjected to additional scrutiny and monitoring by program bureaucrats.

- **Understanding #5:** HIMS will consume your life. Not only is there effectively no relief from the endless AA meetings, Intensive Outpatient Therapy, group aftercare, monitoring meetings, peer monitor calls, yearly psychiatrist evaluations and more, but you will be expected to prioritize "recovery" above even your wife and kids. I was once told by the psychiatrist that I should be prepared to leave my wife – who is my best friend and ever-understanding (sole) source of moral support. Why? Because she stopped drinking when I did and could theoretically relapse, thereby jeopardizing my "recovery." (Please note that I said "the" psychiatrist, not "my" psychiatrist.)

Acceptance, gratitude, humility, serenity and, by unstated implication, passivity are the watchwords of HIMS. The program is a nightmare perversion of Alcoholic Anonymous, in which time-honored tactics for encouraging alcoholics to accept their possibly diminished lot in life (as opposed to becoming bitter and drinking themselves to death over it) are misused by large corporations to make you entirely your company's creature.

I say again: If you are an out-of-control alcoholic, tested positive in a DOT test prior or subsequent to a flight, or had one or more DUIs disqualifying you from holding an FAA medical, these might be realities you have to accept if you intend to continue flying. But denying them will not make them go away.

Top 10 ways to avoid HIMS

1. **Don't** "drink or drug" *at all*: Boring? Yeah, maybe. See 2 through 10 below.

2. **Don't** drive drunk: DUI is the most common HIMS trap.

3. **Don't** test positive: Pushing drinking time close to your report time is the "best" way to trigger a "DOT positive."

4. **Don't** take opioid painkillers or other prescription meds prior to flight, of course, It might be less obvious, but don't take meds that could test positive if they aren't prescribed for *you*, for *your current illness* (yes, even drugs prescribed for you could land you in HIMS if they aren't for your current condition).

5. **Don't** discuss substance use with coworkers … ever.

6. **Don't** "fess up" to those who control your medical certificate unless absolutely necessary. As explained to me by a HIMS Aviation Medical Examiner (AME), attending an AA meeting need not be reportable to the FAA, but a diagnosis of alcohol use disorder is. There are lots of substance abuse programs other than HIMS. Consider finding one administered by people who've never heard of the FAA.

7. **Don't** think your AME is a buddy in whom you can confide. I know pilots who did so and ended up reported to the FAA.

8. **Do** know which substances could test false (or true) positive, which could trigger further scrutiny.

9. **Do** get your own breathalyzer: Know your BAC (blood alcohol content) before you report for duty.

10. **Do** get a lawyer: If the EF5 HIMS tornado is bearing down on you, seek legal advice..

Chapter 2
What to Expect From HIMS

"...she really lets herself go and her painted smile twists, stretches to an open snarl, and she blows up bigger and bigger, big as a tractor, so big I can smell the machinery inside the way you smell a motor pulling too big a load..."
– "Big Nurse" reveals herself in One Flew Over the Cuckoo's Nest

The goal of this book

My objective is to help you avoid HIMS if you can – or survive it if you must. I am a testament to the fact that even the world's biggest "non-Kool-Aid drinker" can survive without sacrificing his soul, if not indefinitely, at least long enough to retire in reasonable comfort.

The two approaches to surviving HIMS:

1. **Buy into the program, lock, stock and barrel:** Many do, bless their little hearts. This approach demands that you be willing (either consciously or through ignorance) to accept the word of HIMS as The Word of God. AA requires you to relinquish control to your "higher power" which it ultimately demands to be "God as you understand him." (Forget the part about accepting AA as your "higher power," or that "G.O.D." can stand for "good orderly direction." That camouflage is intended only to get you hooked on AA. Ultimately, the program will demand that you drop to your knees and pray.)

   In this case, your "higher power" must include HIMS. You must be so fully vested in your recovery from addiction that you are genuinely *happy* with your lot. You will be grateful for each day at work, serenely accepting and overlooking the generally exploitative burdens placed on you by your company. If addiction consumes your life, this is your best bet. In my humble opinion, this replaces substance addiction with addiction to recovery but, of the two, the latter is generally less destructive.

2. **Lie:** As the possibly permanent implementation of AA's credo to "Fake it 'til you make it," this requires you to be a mole from the real world inside the autocracy of HIMS. Make no mistake: Your duplicity must be convincing and complete, with some part of you convinced yourself. You will admit the truth to no one except, perhaps, your close friends and family. At rehab, the credo is "Cooperate to graduate." In HIMS, however, graduation is not forthcoming.

   How many people survive HIMS using this approach is unclear because those who do so admit the truth to few. But I can tell you it works because, with respect to religion, I did it, at least until I decided to do otherwise. "Star of the class" in rehab, "Captain Asshole" became, in the words of one of my fellow inmates, "Captain Awesome." I skipped IOP and went straight to aftercare. Even when the company started trying to take me down, the doctor who administered the program advocated for me (at least initially), saying, "You are fully in compliance with the program, and I'm very pleased with how you are handling all of this."

What you *cannot* do (at least if you plan to survive the program) is engage in half-measures. Perfunctory outlines of your past sins (i.e. Step Five: "Admitted to God, to ourselves, and to another human being the exact nature of our wrongs") will earn you more time in rehab, as I witnessed for two other pilots. At required monthly HIMS monitoring meetings (typically with Employee Assistance Program [EAP] personnel, HIMS bureaucrats, chief pilots and pilots), you may be asked questions about your recovery. Think very carefully about how you respond, since your response will be judged by your superiors and is key to preserving your career.

The goal of HIMS

Forget everything you will be told about how HIMS is intended to help you in your recovery. The goal of HIMS is to make you a more productive, more compliant employee. Period.

Insofar as your recovery goals align with those of the company, your life may be bearable. Smiling doctors will congratulate you on the AA slogans you regurgitate to satisfy their queries; chief pilots will laugh at your self-deprecating "drunk" stories; back-slapping comradery will sweep the room.

The very moment you get crosswise with the company's goals, however, Big Nurse's benevolent smile will morph into a snarl, and you will be told in no uncertain terms to toe the line. If you don't, consequences will soon follow.

What the goal of HIMS is not

One of the burning questions among the five other pilots with me at rehab was "Why?" Namely, why would the company spend the estimated $30,000-$39,000 just for the month in rehab (not including other rehabilitation costs) for each of us instead of just firing us and hiring somebody else?

When our national HIMS pilot representatives, the collaborators of the program, came to the facility for their annual retreat and to tell us their "stories," they insisted, "It's cheaper for the company to rehabilitate you than to hire somebody new."

Bullshit. Let's look at the numbers, shall we? Between my near-celebrity rehab center (one non-pilot left for Betty Ford because we didn't have a swimming pool), psychiatric and cognitive evaluations, sick time, disability pay during the nine months I wasn't working, IOP (Intensive Outpatient treatment, which admittedly I was not required to do), group aftercare, paid time during return-to-service training, simulator and ground training cost, the princely sum they pay the contractor who administers the HIMS program and much more, my WAG ("wild-assed guess") is that getting me back to work cost my company close to $250,000 ... which, incidentally, doesn't break my heart in the slightest.

By comparison, what do you suppose it costs to train a new pilot to replace me? With simulator and ground training costs, transportation, and payroll, perhaps $50,000, meaning they could hire five new pilots for the cost of re-educating me. So why do they do it?

Control, baby. It's all about control.

My wife doubted this, so I reminded her of a story that happened a few years ago: I was a Boeing 737 captain when an airplane showed up at the gate with both the yaw damper[1] and autopilot legally inoperative per the Minimum Equipment List or "MEL."[2] Moreover, the entire northeastern U.S. was experiencing moderate turbulence at high altitude. The captain who brought in the airplane described the combination of turbulence and inoperative components as "like a monkey fucking a football."

Considering I also had a green co-pilot fresh out of new hire training, I refused the aircraft. But the mechanic working the flight didn't seem to agree: "You have to fly it. It's legal," he said.

"I don't have to fly shit," was my response. "I'm the Pilot in Command and I deem the operation unsafe. End of story."

He called the chief pilot, who came out to the aircraft, and the process was repeated. In the end, the flight cancelled and 120-odd people blew their connections. Thanks to the FAA and my union contract, I suffered no repercussions. As to what that cancellation cost the company, I leave it to your imagination but note that cancellations are very expensive. Say, $50,000?

Over a 35-year airline career utterly free of accidents, incidents and regulatory violations, "Captain Asshole" similarly refused flights due to poor weather, inadequate fuel loads and unsafe cargo (the latter comprised trays of US Mail loaded aboard my aircraft at Washington National Airport after 9/11 and simultaneously with the discovery of anthrax at the Brentwood mail facility in Washington). I did so secure in the knowledge that my airline couldn't do anything to me. (They did remove me without pay from the Washington flight, but I filed a grievance with the union.)

Now let's imagine a pilot in HIMS doing the same thing. First, he would probably get a call from his chief pilot, saying: "We think you have anger management issues. We are going to review your case with the Quad.[3]" Said pilot would be removed from the line pending review. He might then be sent to a psychiatrist for evaluation. The net result might well be the loss of his Special Issuance Medical Certificate (SI). At the very least, the following lesson would be imparted: Don't rock the boat.

Even the HIMS program website admits, "As in any health care decision, cost of treatment is an important factor. A 28-day residential treatment program is, understandably, quite expensive. But research has shown that for every dollar spent on treatment and continuing care, companies receive $2 – $11 in return." What the site neglects to mention is the *source* of that 200 to 1100 percent return.

What companies get from HIMS is a supply of pilots fearful that anything they do to anger the company might end their careers and who are therefore extorted into accepting inconvenient, uncomfortable or even potentially unsafe operations that pilots fully protected by working agreements, and therefore insulated from consequences, might refuse. While the cost of training replacement pilots might be peanuts, the comparative cost of cancellations and delays is not. Industry averages suggest that bad customer experiences during disruptions can cost a single airline as much as $62 million per year, making HIMS chump change by comparison.

Given HIMS' profitability, it is little surprise that airlines are now stressing "early identification" of ostensible substance abusers in order to suck as many pilots as possible into the vortex of the HIMS tornado. Whose lives they destroy in the process is, of course, unimportant.

Aviation safety & HIMS

"But," you might ask, "shouldn't passengers be entitled to flights secure in the knowledge that pilots aren't flying impaired?"

Of course. But that isn't the purpose of HIMS. If the FAA and airlines were concerned only with safety, the solution would be simple: Require completion of a sobriety test prior to the first flight of each working day. For each flight, both pilots must presently declare themselves "fit for flight," usually electronically. If that declaration contained a sobriety test, safety from impaired flying would be assured. But even the random drug and alcohol testing presently conducted by the Department of Transportation (DOT) doesn't do that. A proportion of flight crews are tested randomly each day *after* flight, making such testing a measure of sobriety for *a flight which already took place.* Does that sound like genuine concern for passengers' safety or just bureaucratic butt-covering?

Captain's authority? Not so much

Remember FAR 91.3? "The pilot in command of an aircraft is directly responsible for, and is the final authority as to, the operation of that aircraft." Yeah, well, forget that. As noted earlier, once you are sucked into HIMS, you will be questioned, intimidated and possibly relieved of duty whenever your exercise of "captain's authority" diverges from the interests of the company.

Privacy as you know it is over

From the moment you enter HIMS, your every word and deed may be measured and recorded. Do not think for a moment that you can make an "off-the-record" remark. Whatever you say to any counselor, monitor, doctor or peer may end up in your permanent record to be viewed by untold numbers of bureaucrats – a permanent record which will grow to include your age of first sexual experience, how many sex partners you've had, whether you are currently monogamous, the reasons for your divorce(s), the embarrassments of your childhood, your bowel function, and *sooo* much more.

Reports on monthly monitoring meetings with your chief pilot, HIMS bureaucrats, peer monitors and others will include not only whether you attended (generally mandatory), but also whether you arrived on time, how you dressed, and whether what you "shared" was sufficiently grateful and humble.

A group therapy counselor once asked me about my "goals" in treatment. When I couldn't come up with much, she thoughtfully said: "Why don't we say you want to improve your interpersonal skills?" When the company later decided to get my Special Issuance Medical Certificate withdrawn because I was deemed insufficiently supplicant, guess what was featured in the FAA record as part of their rationalization for getting my medical pulled?

Conclusions made by your overseers and entered into your permanent record are by no means limited to what you say. Your mood will be observed and interpreted, your speech will be evaluated, even what you wear to an appointment is fair game. If you express irritation at an idiotic question, you can expect a little black mark to be permanently enshrined in your file.

Do not expect the information reflected in your records to be accurate. When I finally started down the track to sue my employer for violating the Americans with Disabilities Act, I requested my medical record from the FAA (a six-inch stack of paper), from the psychiatrist (75 pages), and from the quacks contracted to administer the program (1500 pages). What I received was rife with inaccuracies and mischaracterizations of things I had naively admitted – mischaracterizations which invariably coincided with the pre-ordained and self-serving agendas of these ostensible "professionals."

Oh, did I forget to mention that both the HIMS bureaucrats and the psychiatrist refused to release my own medical records to me until they got a lawyer letter?

'Big Nurse' and the 'Big F.I.B.'

Like Nurse Ratched in *One Flew Over the Cuckoo's Nest,* for as long as you swallow your dose of pablum, regurgitate the AA slogans you are fed and regularly vow humility, powerlessness and gratitude, "Big Nurse" will smile benevolently upon you. You will be complimented on your recovery and will hear of the many benefits awaiting you.

But the moment you refuse your meds and demand "I want *my* cigarettes" (see the "Cuckoo's Nest" scene on YouTube), the previously nice orderlies will restrain you and drag you away in an exercise of what I call "The Big F.I.B.," as in Fear, Intimidation, and Blackmail.

❏ **Fear:** If you are like most pilots, you fear losing your career and with it, the benefits your kids enjoy, your lifestyle, your house, maybe even your marriage. The specialized (and expensive) training you sweated for to become a pilot doesn't translate particularly well to other careers. Most of the guys I met in HIMS who were awaiting their SI and who didn't have a company disability policy ended up working in places like Home Depot. Then, of course, we have the prestige of being an airline pilot (or, even better, **Airline Captain**). You might have spent a few decades enjoying that moment at the cocktail party where a new acquaintance asks, "So, what do you do?" One ex-wife used to routinely refer to me as "The Captain." Pretty nice ego boost, eh?

❏ **Intimidation**: Rest assured HIMS personnel know they have your career in their hands, and will cheerfully remind you of that whenever the need arises. If you step out of line, you will be told your non-compliance could be "career-ending." You will be told that short of hospitalization or death, you must never miss a HIMS meeting, no matter what. Your compliance with testing will be carefully monitored. Your every word at HIMS meetings or to the shrink will be recorded and assessed. If you think you are "under the radar," you are probably wrong.

- **Blackmail:** These are not idle threats. Take it from one who knows: Abstinence and compliance with the mechanical requirements of the program are not enough and won't save you from Big Nurse if you are insufficiently humble. Any one of the unholy triad of your company, HIMS personnel and doctors can, at any time, decide that your attitude isn't to their liking and get your SI yanked.

Release from fear

After raising the issue of potential non-compliance by company personnel with the Americans with Disabilities Act (ADA) at a HIMS meeting, I was removed from line flying under the pretext of having had one too many disagreements with incompetent customer service agents. (In truth, the company had me in its sights ever since a union slowdown years before.)

Off to the shrink for me, where I learned that my ego was too large, and that I felt entirely too "entitled" as pilot in command of my aircraft. This, the good doctor assured me, was a backslide in my recovery. He even alluded to my previous reference to my occasional tendencies as "Captain Asshole" – a characterization I made in confidence during a HIMS meeting which was apparently relayed to him by my chief pilot, just as the same chief pilot had relayed it to others who were unaware of my participation in HIMS.

When I had the audacity to disagree, the good doctor pulled out the DSM (Diagnostic and Statistical Manual of Psychological Disorders) and threatened me with a diagnosis of "narcissistic personality disorder" if I persisted. The diagnosis, he assured me, would be potentially "career-ending."

Apparently, the cure for "narcissistic personality disorder" is more AA. I was remanded to review Steps 4 and 5 with my sponsor (whom the good doctor telephoned, for good measure), and to return in a month to see whether my attitude had changed. Incidentally, during that month I was removed from line flying and forced to exhaust my sick bank. At a WAG, that visit to the doctor visit cost me about $20,000.

Unfortunately for Dr. Shrink, AA provided me with an epiphany he didn't anticipate. During a meeting in which we read passages from *As Bill Sees It* pertaining to courage and fear, it occurred to me that I was far too dependent on my role as airline captain. My "share" went something like this:

> *"Like others here, I have lived in fear. Ironically, however, my fear arose **after** I stopped drinking, and was instilled in me by the highly regimented HIMS program to which my airline remanded me if I wanted to be allowed to finish out my career. Yesterday, despite two years of perfect compliance with the program, after pointing out a potential company violation of the ADA, the shrink I was sent to threatened me with a diagnosis of "narcissistic personality disorder" unless my attitude improved. But today, I had an epiphany; namely, that I have been too wedded to my role as airline captain, and that if the good doctor chooses to follow through on his threat, I will be okay. Thanks to you, I no longer live in fear."*

My sponsor later congratulated me, noting that I had recognized I had a choice (albeit an expensive one) not to participate in the program. After that, "The Big F.I.B." had no power over me.

A novel I read, written by a Vietnam vet, described a commander who, prior to the Tet Offensive of 1968, required his leaders to write their own obituaries in order to accept (and therefore alleviate) their fear of death. It is a lesson HIMS pilots would do well to consider.

The five lies about HIMS you will hear

1. **"HIMS is no big deal":** As noted previously, it is a *very* big deal, and will dominate – even control – your life for the duration of your sentence to the Gulag. AA is the first to note that "recovery is a full-time job." In HIMS, proving to *others* that you are recovering adds yet another "full-time job." While AA might require regularly attending meetings, meeting with your sponsor, and doing occasional service work, HIMS adds to that, at a minimum:

   - Initial psychiatric evaluation, including PEth (blood) testing for long-term metabolites of alcohol;
   - A minimum of 28-30 days in an inpatient rehabilitation facility (I've heard of at least one airline which requires 35 days);
   - 90 AA meetings in 90 days after release from inpatient treatment, certified by signed forms returned at HIMS monthly monitoring meetings, after which you will be required to continue AA meetings (typically three or four per week);
   - Intensive Outpatient treatment (IOP), typically 3 days per week, 3 hours per day for 3 months;
   - Group aftercare indefinitely, typically at a rate of four times per month prior to issuance of your SI (Special Issuance Medical Certificate), and twice monthly thereafter (or more, depending on your airline and SI requirements);
   - Monthly monitoring meetings between medical personnel, EAP personnel, chief pilot representatives, and pilots;
   - Substance abuse monitoring, typically by blowing into an electronic "Soberlink®" device every four waking hours for some period, after which monitoring typically reverts to random urinalysis requiring you to drive to testing sites fourteen times per year;
   - Daylong (and expensive) cognitive testing, along with another psychiatric evaluation, prior to submitting your package to the FAA for your SI;
   - Four calls per month to your "peer monitor," another pilot in the program;

- Regular meetings with your AA sponsor, including working the steps; and
- An annual package, including yet another psychiatric evaluation, from your HIMS personnel documenting your participation in the program and recommending you for re-issuance of your SI.

2. **"Rehab is easy":** If you want a vague idea of what rehabilitation will be like, watch the movie *28 Days* (which was very popular in the TV room of my rehab facility, by the way). First, there is the considerable cost of rehab facilities. Your health insurance might partially cover it, but it is reasonable to expect deductibles and co-pays of $2500 or more. (Obviously, check your policy.)

In rehab, get used to being treated like a criminal. It is presumed that you can't be trusted. Anything you say is presumed to be a lie (a presumption which will continue long into recovery). Any maintenance medications you take, however benign, will be locked up at Big Nurse's desk, and you will line up twice a day with the other inmates to take what they have approved. You will likely room with someone else, and you will have an enforced curfew and mealtimes and, in general, highly regimented activities. Oh, yes: Your person, your room and your belongings will be routinely searched. Privacy is non-existent.

Then there is the utter isolation from your life. Just you and the other inmates with, initially, no contact with the outside world. Kiss goodbye to your cell phone for a month, as well as your laptop and other electronic devices. For the first 72 hours, you will speak to no one on the outside, not even your family. After that, you may be allowed to use one of the few phone lines in the facility and, at prescribed times, typically in the evening, you might get limited privileges to use the facility computer or watch television (in a common TV room, of course).

If allowed at all, smokers can expect to check their cigarettes at Big Nurse's desk, getting them rationed back only for designated smoking times for a few minutes each day. Cruelest of all (at least for me), at my facility, caffeine was *verboten*, creating a lovely underground trade in Starbucks VIA packets. (Guilty as charged: I was a Starbucks "pusher.") But all that pales by comparison to the obligation to bare your soul to strangers ... each day. Piece of cake.

3. **"We have the best HIMS program in the industry"**: Best for whom, exactly? Some airlines (especially mine, by the reports of aviation lawyers) are infamous for using medical certificates – or the withholding thereof – as means for discipline and for ridding themselves of pilots they deem to be troublemakers, union contracts be damned. Unfortunately, you might not get to choose between HIMS programs, so you could be pretty much stuck with what your airline uses, but I suggest that you not take the sales pitch at face value.

4. **"You can get your medical back in as few as six months"**: Excuse me, but bullshit. I did everything as near as possible to perfectly, including completing the requirements in five months, after which the FAA sat on it for an additional four months. As a bonus, the FAA doctor in charge actually called me (a rare occurrence, by all accounts) on a *Saturday* to tell me he was recommending that they approve my package. But beyond the satisfaction of knowing my tax dollar was buying weekend duty from the feds, it didn't speed up the process and still took three months longer than I was promised, nine months in all. Had I been required to undergo IOE, it would likely have been longer.

5. **"You will only be subject to monitoring for three years"**: More bullshit. Ignoring, for a moment, that the duration of monitoring will depend on the severity of your transgression (with particularly naughty pilots earning monitoring for the remainder of their careers), word has it that the FAA now routinely requires five years or more for everybody.

Company abuses

Once the ol' HIMS EF5 tornado sucks you in, it doesn't let go. One individual I spoke with withdrew from the program and got his own Independent Medical Sponsor (IMS). In response, the contractor administering the HIMS program for the company reportedly falsified his records and misrepresented his history to the FAA.

If online doctor rating services are to be believed, the shrink my company planned to use to get rid of me (unsuccessfully, I might add) had reportedly falsified a pilot's urinalysis results. The same shrink also ended up at the center of a legal case in which he was reportedly paid a large sum to diagnose a safety whistleblower with a career-ending personality disorder. Despite ethics complaints, as I write this he is still a prominent HIMS psychiatrist.

Another individual was shocked when supervisory personnel met him at the airplane he had just flown in and escorted him outside security after taking his airline identification card. It seems his PeTh test had come in with a (false) positive, and he had to prove his abstinence by purchasing his own independent test. He eventually got his job back ... only slightly scarred.

Bottom line: if you ask questions or make waves in any way, expect to be immediately and brutally targeted by your overseers. To paraphrase the "Star Trek" line, "Resistance is futile; you will be assimilated."

The good news

Although this book is not, by and large, a glowing review of HIMS, there are some silver linings. If you are truly in need of treatment, you will get it. Twelve-step facilitation therapy isn't particularly effective, but it does help some people. And if you are a "get-along" type, you may thrive in the program, albeit with a life very different from anything you previously envisioned.

The three advantages to HIMS:

1. **HIMS is a boatload easier than restoring your medical by yourself**: I met one pilot in rehab who was abstaining from alcohol and restoring his medical himself. Even though he had invested $50,000 in getting his SI, he had been rejected twice. He had an alternative job, because he was already about three unsuccessful years into the effort and had a fat binder of paperwork (but still no SI) to show for his efforts.

2. **Treatment is generally first-class:** In the substance abuse field, substandard treatment and frauds abound. I had one doctor tell me he could restore my medical in just a few months independently, neatly ignoring FAR 67.107, which stipulates two years free from substance abuse prior to restoration of a medical certificate unless enrolled in HIMS. He also pushed a recovery center (from which he undoubtedly got a kickback), that I later learned was a complete dump. By contrast, the FAA has signed off on HIMS programs. The quality of treatment facilities may vary, but is generally industry standard or better.

3. **You can't "cheat":** If you are truly a substance abuser who can't quit any other way, HIMS stands a better chance of being "the cure" than other methods. For one thing, if you cheat, you will get caught. EtG (Ethyl Glucuronide) testing, to which you will be randomly subjected about 14 times per year, theoretically detects alcohol in the blood for three days. In truth, it is more like five days or longer. Your company may supplement it with periodic PEth testing, which detects markers for alcohol for several weeks. This makes cheating a no-brainer. I once had a cab driver, who might have gotten a cut from a bar he was recommending, keep pushing me to go to a happy hour. I finally asked him, "How much would that Margarita cost you?" He responded, "I dunno, five bucks, maybe?" My answer was, "Well it would cost me about $300,000. Does that sound like a reasonable price to you?"

The cost of HIMS… and it ain't just dollars and cents

The financial cost of HIMS doesn't begin to cover what you will actually pay. By far, the greater cost will be emotional, and for many, that cost is too high.

- **Your self-esteem:** If you are like most pilots, you have a bit of an ego. Many would regard it as necessary for the job. Early in my career I read a book on air transport operations which made the point that you need an ego to strap 150 tons of metal to your ass and blast off into the sky. But that won't be acceptable in HIMS, where both AA and the program will do their best to tear down your ego and replace it with humility. "Humility," goes the slogan you will hear endlessly, "isn't thinking less of yourself, it's thinking about yourself less." Bullshit. Thinking less of yourself is *exactly* what they seek. You will have your nose rubbed in your many flaws for the rest of your life, all for your own good, of course. If your ego and your flaws are impediments to your life, that might be a good thing. But this is a "one-size-fits-all" approach, regardless of whether your personality traits present a problem or not.

- **Your personality:** As one of the counselors at rehab was fond of saying, "The only thing you have to change is everything." When I lamented to my therapist that I didn't want to change everything, that in fact I was quite happy with who I was, thanks, I was told to "Just take what works and discard the rest." Unfortunately, that is not acceptable in HIMS. For the program, nothing less than complete transformation of your personality will suffice. You are, after all, just a drunk.

- **Your relationships:** You will be told to prioritize recovery above even your friends and family. Your drinking buddies are definitely persona non grata, even if they have been lifelong companions. Too much temptation, you see. The demanded quarantine might include not just your friends, but also your spouse. I was told to consider leaving my endlessly loving and understanding wife, who sympathetically quit drinking when I did and even joined AA, because a theoretical relapse on her part might cause me a setback. Had I heeded that sage advice, you probably wouldn't be reading this because I would likely be dead.

- **Possibly, your life:** I don't just mean the quality of your life, I mean life itself. You will be given a role model to live up to, one of sobriety, humility, gratitude, serenity, and ostensible joy. Some participants despair at their inability to live up to that ideal. Some kill themselves. A casual search finds no statistics for how many pilots in HIMS have committed suicide; I suspect neither the FAA nor the airlines want to know. But I can tell you that in my crew base alone, we said our little prayers for about two per year. Whether that is beyond the normal range of suicide for substance abusers, I leave to your imagination, but I can tell you that I heard of no such suicides in my home AA group.

'Powerless' pilots?

At a monthly monitoring meeting, I responded to the required "share of the month" by raising concerns about the inherent conflict between the "powerlessness" demanded by AA and the safety-related need for pilots to be absolutely empowered to control their aircraft at all times. One pilot claimed to have solved the issue by shedding "ego" and adopting "humility," but never quite mentioned why being safely in control of an airplane equates to "ego." Another allowed that while he was powerless over some things, he knew the difference between circumstances, since he was clearly powerless if his "wing fell off." I responded that, far from "acceptance," if my "wing fell off," USA Today wouldn't be able to print my cockpit voice recorder tape because it would contain "Fly, you Sonofabitch!" all the way to the ground. But seriously, the fundamental flaw in their theory is that "the wisdom to know the difference" is neither "wisdom," nor necessarily clear. Regardless, HIMS and AA condition pilots to default to "powerlessness," often to the decrement of air safety.

References:

1. A yaw damper is a device used on transport category aircraft to damp the rolling and yawing oscillations known as "Dutch roll."

2. The Minimum Equipment List (MEL) allows airlines to obtain relief from Federal Aviation Regulations requiring that all equipment installed on the aircraft be operative for flight, stipulating which equipment may be inoperable along with required procedures and conditions under which the aircraft may be operated.

3. Terms for the HIMS programs may vary between airlines. At ours, the "Quad" referred to interaction between company management, the doctor acting as Independent Medical Sponsor (IMS), Employee Assistance Program personnel, and a pilot representative.

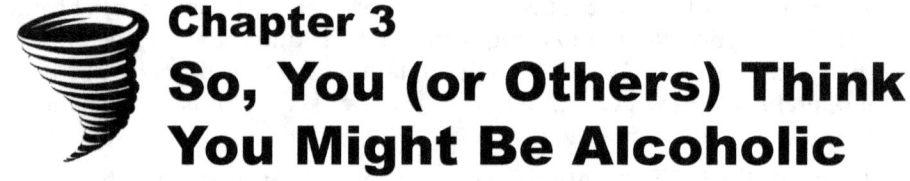

Chapter 3
So, You (or Others) Think You Might Be Alcoholic

Voluntary participation?

Disclaimer: I am not here to diagnose you. I am not a substance abuse professional and have no particular expertise in the field. If you need help from a professional, get it ASAP.

Were it me...

I can only say that were *I* to wake up hungover one day, and decided I needed help, *I* would seek it out from somebody who had never heard of the FAA. Whatever its flaws, Alcoholics Anonymous specializes in that sort of thing and helps thousands of people get sober each and every year ... anonymously.

Knowing what I now do, even if I decided I needed rehab, I might be prone to foot the (admittedly very high) bill myself without telling a soul beyond those with "a need to know." I might even take a month off using as a reason, say, bursitis of the shoulder or something equally difficult to positively diagnose; something which does not permanently impact your medical certificate. But, of course, that's just me.

> **Be aware**
>
> It is a crime to lie to the FAA on your medical form (Form 8500-8). In 2018, a federal grand jury indicted four airline pilots for making false statements to the government. They were accused of submitting forms to the FAA denying the existence of medical conditions for which they were receiving disability benefits from the U.S. Department of Veterans Affairs and were charged with "Making a false statement, in violation of 18 U.S.C. § 1001(a)(2)." One critical factor is whether you have been diagnosed with a substance abuse or mental disorder. Bearing in mind that I am not a lawyer and nothing in this book constitutes legal advice, I have been advised by professionals in the field that the diagnosis is what makes your problem subject to reporting requirements.[1]

I will also not advise you on disclosure of such things to the FAA during renewal of your medical certificate, but I will note that HIPAA generally prevents the release of such information and, if you ultimately enroll in HIMS, you will likely get a penalty-free "disclosure amnesty" to revise what you may or may not have disclosed previously.

> **The story of Pilot X**
>
> I knew a certain pilot very well. Years back, he underwent a divorce, during which he became depressed. He called his union's aeromedical department to find out the implications of what he thought he might be facing. When told that a diagnosis of depression would earn a two-year loss of his medical, and that the prescription of anti-depressants would further extend the loss, he sought counseling from somebody unfamiliar with the FAA, got a referral to a psychiatrist, and picked up a number of samples of an SSRI (selective serotonin reuptake inhibitor), which he determined beforehand to have minimal side effects, and which he took on an interim basis until switching to an over-the-counter solution such as St. John's Wort or SAM-e. Just sayin'…

Are you a 'drunk'?

As for judging whether you are, indeed, an alcoholic, I would note that by current standards, most of the nation of France (42 liters of wine per person per year on average, with an alcohol consumption rate 35% greater than ours) should take that white chip of surrender. Given that

France continues to function (a few socialist uprisings and military misadventures aside), I would offer that current American standards are, in a word, idiotic.

Nonetheless, these are the standards by which you will be judged, so here is what Barton Pakull, M.D., former FAA Chief Psychiatrist, considered to be the criteria for alcoholism[2], thereby rendering you ineligible for an FAA medical:

Evidence of tolerance:

1. Blood alcohol content (BAC) of more than 0.15 without overt evidence of intoxication.
2. Consumption of 750 ml of liquor or equivalent amount of beer or wine daily for two or more consecutive days
3. Blackouts.
4. A blood alcohol level greater than 0.25 percent at any time.

Evidence of psychological dependence:

1. When you begin drinking, are you in a hurry for the first drink? (Gulping drinks.)
2. Do you wish to continue drinking after your friends have had enough?
3. Have you felt "remorse" after drinking?
4. Do you often drink more than four drinks a day and feel ill at ease when you don't?
5. Do you ever start out to just have two or three drinks and wind up drunk when you do not intend to?
6. Do you find that you cannot predict how much you will drink after your first drink on a social occasion?
7. Do you ever promise yourself you'll stop drinking or slow down and then break that promise?
8. Do you drink more heavily when you are under pressure or after a disappointment or quarrel?
9. Do you require a drink the next morning to calm your nerves?

10. Have you had to promise someone close to you that you will "cut down" on your drinking?
11. Have you begun to prefer to drink alone?
12. Have you had more than one bender in the past six months?
13. Do you use tranquilizers during periods of time when you are unwilling or unable to drink alcohol?

The American Psychiatric Association has not done you any favors. The most recent version of the Diagnostic and Statistical Manual of Mental Disorders (DSM-5)[3] differs from DSM-4 by combining the less serious (and not medically disqualifying) "alcohol abuse" with the more serious (and disqualifying) "alcohol dependence" into a single disqualifying "alcohol use disorder" (AUD) with sub-categories of mild, moderate or severe. For the AUD criteria of DSM-5, see Appendix B.

What I would not do...

What I would *not* do, if faced with possible options, would be to call my Employee Assistance Program (EAP), "Project Wingman" (or whatever equivalent your union may have), or my union HIMS representatives and say, "So, do you think I'm a drunk?" because regardless of the actuality, I can assure you their answer will be "yes," and you will soon be without a medical certificate.

You may have seen the compelling videos of pilots who couldn't get off the couch due to depression and called their troubled pilot program, which "saved" them by giving them the help they needed to return to work. What the video does *not* say is that their phone call probably got them up to two years out of work (more if anti-depressants were prescribed) at reduced or non-existent pay.

I've spoken to several pilots who self-reported to HIMS. Most eventually regretted it. Some ended up without a career. If I felt potentially suicidal, out of control, or in any way out of options, I would certainly reach out to whomever I needed to in order to survive, but HIMS would not be my first choice.

> **The story of 'Shawn'**
>
> "Shawn" was a mechanic for my airline, who decided he had an alcohol problem and voluntarily sought help from our Employee Assistance Program (EAP). Although he was not subject to HIMS per se, he was remanded to rehab just the same. I knew him when he came in, and he was upbeat, intelligent, and willing to embrace recovery.
>
> Unfortunately, his equally alcoholic long-term, live-in girlfriend was not interested in sobriety, and in group therapy sessions, the counselors began pressuring him to leave her. Over the next few weeks, this upbeat guy gradually became desultory, resentful and non-compliant. On one of the little supervised group outings to the beach, he and another patient went "walkabout" (a serious no-no in rehab). He went walkabout again during an outdoor family visit. Not long after, he was dismissed from rehab and, presumably, from his job.

Not-so-voluntary participation

If you are tagged by your airline or the FAA, your options are considerably more limited. If you test DOT positive on a drug or alcohol screen prior or subsequent to flight, your options are most limited of all. In such cases, you will also face an emergency revocation of your pilot certificates. (See the sidebar later in this chapter.)

Indeed, if you fly internationally, be aware that in other countries – particularly the UK – alcohol limits are lower than in the US, and officials aggressively look for pilots reporting for duty over the limit, including waiting until you enter the aircraft to test you in order to prove intent to fly while under the influence. As I write this, an airline pilot was just arrested in Manchester. Another pilot is reportedly serving a ten-month prison sentence in Japan.

Even in the US, I would counsel pilots to be very careful about pushing alcohol limits. In truth, just because you adhere to your airline policy, which might be as little as "eight hours, bottle to throttle," at report time you may still exceed the very low BAC of 0.04 which results in an

FAA violation, or the even lower BAC of 0.02 which would cause you to be relieved of duty.

Let's talk about that 0.02 BAC limit which supposedly just relieves you of duty: In rehab, I met one airline captain who was remanded to HIMS because he had a chronic limp, which a customer service agent helpfully reported as potential impairment prior to his flight. Although he only tested 0.02 – in violation of company policy but not FARs – the HIMS vortex sucked him in anyway, so don't think being below the FAA legal limit will protect you.

If you enjoy a cocktail or two on overnights, I would note that electronic blood alcohol measuring devices are now available online for less than $150. Were it me, I might carry one and consider calling in sick in case I misjudged and accidentally exceeded 0.02 BAC prior to my scheduled report time. But that's just me ...

Five things to do if being forced into HIMS:

1. **Seek legal advice:** Although this might be a no-brainer for anyone facing a DOT positive test, plenty of people sucked into the HIMS vortex do not test positive. The possibilities for arbitrarily getting trapped by HIMS are, unfortunately, myriad and increasing. I ended up in the program after nothing more than a company-demanded (and contractually mandated) physical exam resulting from an argument with a hotel security guard. Another pilot I know was reported by his vindictive ex-wife during divorce.

   Every day, naïve pilots who assume the system wants to "help" them waive the protections afforded by an attorney, generally to their own detriment. A Google search will reveal plenty of lawyers specializing in FAA medical compliance issues, including HIMS. Some are better than others, and some predict a rosier outcome than others, so seek advice from half a dozen or more, keeping notes from each, until you arrive at a consensus on the best way to approach your situation.

Incidentally, by "seek legal advice," I mean legal advice *beyond* your union, if you are so represented. Not to say you might not ultimately use union lawyers, but never forget that they work for the union, not you, and their interests might not always align with yours. Yes, retaining outside counsel will cost money, potentially serious money. But now is not the time to be cheap. Spending a few thousand now could save you a few *hundred* thousand later.

2. **Quit drinking immediately:** Most pilots don't realize they may be subjected to phosphatidylethanol (PEth) blood testing, and they especially don't know that PEth levels can remain elevated for *a month or more* after consuming alcohol. Worse, elevated PEth can be detected for up to *12 days or more* after a single episode of alcohol consumption. That means if you "tie one on" just *once* prior to being subjected to a PEth test, you could be diagnosed as an alcoholic and forced into HIMS on penalty of revocation of your medical, despite the fact that a single case of alcohol *abuse* might not equate to alcohol *dependence.*

   That was what happened to me. I consumed alcohol only once in the 30 days prior to testing (I assumed the testing would be EtG testing, which measures a much shorter period of time), yet ended up being diagnosed as alcohol dependent solely on the basis of the test, not my interview with the psychiatrist.

   If you have a problem quitting immediately, go to AA and pick up that white chip of surrender (or use some other method to stop drinking). If that doesn't work, you might consider whether you are indeed so heavily addicted that you *need* an all-consuming and dictatorial program like HIMS.

3. **Don't volunteer:** If you are a union member, and your union participates in a HIMS program, here is what you will probably hear: "You should get the substance abuse evaluation from the psychiatrist we contract rather than the one the company picks because he will be more prone to give you a fair shake." Nonsense. In *neither*

case are you the psychiatrist's patient, and the diagnosis he or she renders will not be for you, it will be for the company, HIMS and the FAA. I made the mistake of listening to the union HIMS representatives and ended up with a diagnosis which would likely have been no worse from a doctor designated by the company.

4. **Run the clock:** See items 2 and 3 above. Disciplinary and medical actions, particularly with unions involved, can take several weeks to wind through their various levels and hearings. Those are weeks during which metabolites of alcohol gradually leave your body.

5. **Be very careful what you say to the psychiatrist:** Whether you choose to lie, I leave to you. Suffice to say that you should go into the evaluation with a very clear idea of what the substance abuse industry considers to be signs of addiction and be prepared for an interview designed to entrap you. Start by Googling "What to expect during a substance abuse evaluation" and also check the list of questions and tests typically used in evaluations under "Substance abuse/dependence evaluation" in Chapter 6. At the conclusion of my evaluation, the psychiatrist finished my interview by saying: "I hope I never have to see you again." Had I known items 1-4 above, he wouldn't have.

> **Recent changes for 'DOT positives'**
>
> Effective October 1, 2018, the FAA made available a "prompt settlement" policy for first-time violators who: (1) Receive a verified positive result for a DOT-required drug test; (2) Receive a DOT-required alcohol test result with alcohol concentration of .04 or above; (3) Refuse to submit to a DOT-required drug or alcohol test in violation of FARs; or (4) Act or attempt to act as a crewmember of an aircraft in commercial operations in violation of specified FARs.
>
> The good news is that you might shortcut the protracted time the FAA normally takes for a certificate action, meaning you could get back to flying sooner. The bad news is that you must: (1) Agree to immediately surrender your certificates and not apply for a new certificate for at least one year; (2) Waive any rights to appeal; and (3) Agree to enter HIMS. You must request prompt settlement within 10 days of the underlying violation.
>
> Source: https://www.fordharrison.com/airline-industry-alert-faa-enacts-prompt-settlement-policy-for-pilots-who-are-first-time-violators-of-drug-and-alcohol-testing-regulations

References:

1. Sandy Murdock, "Airline Pilots need not lie to FAA about Mental Health to keep Flying," *JDA Journal*, November 12, 2018, http://jdasolutions.aero/blog/airline-pilots-need-not-lie-faa-mental-health-keep-flying/
2. Barton Pakull M.D., "Alcoholism and Aviation Medical Certification", *Alcoholism: Clinical & Experimental Research*, January 1978, https://onlinelibrary.wiley.com/doi/abs/10.1111/j.1530-0277.1978.tb04692.x
3. *Diagnostic and Statistical Manual of Mental Disorders* (5th ed.; DSM–5; American Psychiatric Association, 2013).

Chapter 4
The Recovery Industry and You

"No experimental studies unequivocally demonstrate the effectiveness of AA or TSF [Twelve Step Facilitation] approaches for reducing alcohol dependence or problems."
– Ferri & Davoli: "Alcoholics Anonymous and Other 12-Step Programmes for Alcohol Dependence"[1]

All is not rosy in The Land of Recovery. A documentary entitled *The Business of Recovery*,[2] for example, "examines the untold billions that are being made off of families in crisis," saying that many in the industry "prey" on addicts. Even the ostensibly mainstream Alcoholics Anonymous (AA) draws fire by many, both for its cult-like structure and for the fact that it essentially mandates religion. Thirty-six-year former AA member Monica Richardson and her site, leavingaa.com, document a variety of malfeasance conducted in the name of recovery. Richardson also made a documentary of AA abuses entitled *The 13th Step*[3] and does a podcast called "Safe Recovery."[4]

For a better understanding of the "Minnesota Model" which rules the substance abuse treatment industry, one should look at its origins. As outlined by award-winning journalist Joe Miller in *US of AA: How the Twelve Steps Hijacked the Science of Alcoholism*[5], our current treatment standard got its start in 1939 when Minneapolis alcoholic and AA advocate Pat Cronin got himself certified by the state of Minnesota as an "alcoholic counselor" and, despite lacking qualifications, helped create "Pioneer House" and later "Hazeldon," both early rehab facilities. Says Miller: "…patients received a course of remedy that consisted almost exclusively of AA tenets – a thorough working of steps one through five – and this method would come to be known as the 'Minnesota Model,' the standard for alcoholism treatment in America."

The ironies of substance abuse treatment

Irony #1: You will be told that addiction is a disease, a medical condition resulting from chronic over-stimulation of dopamine pathways in the brain. But as an addict, you will be treated like a reprobate. You will be called a "drunk" and considered a habitual liar who cannot be trusted to spend a moment alone, much less control your own life. Counselors will demand to know how long you have been "sober" as though you had been continuously intoxicated beforehand. Some allege that such treatment is deliberately used to shame you into compliance.

Irony #2: Harkening to medieval bloodletting and magical charms, your *medical* condition will be treated using *religion* and *spirituality*. In rehab, my overseers touted the excellent movie *Pleasure Unwoven*[6] by Dr. Kevin McCauley, an Air Force flight surgeon who himself became addicted. The film expounds on the neuroendocrine mechanisms of addiction. Despite this disease model, however, "Twelve-Step Facilitation" (TSF) treatment programs still dominate the industry, trying – and generally failing – to treat physiological problems with religious, moral and spiritual solutions.

As part of your spiritual treatment, you will be forbidden to control your own life. As a drunk, you will be told you are powerless and must therefore relinquish control to a "higher power," ostensibly a higher power of your choosing but, in reality, bearing a remarkable resemblance to a Christian God. (As previously noted, how your newfound lack of control should be reconciled with the fact that an airline pilot had damned well better be in control is never entirely clear, and you will be discouraged from asking.)

One thing not to do in substance abuse treatment

Don't even think of saying, "I'm not addicted." As noted elsewhere in this book, I met one HIMS victim, ensnared by refusing the breathalyzer on a DUI motor vehicle stop, who insisted he was not an alcoholic, that he had just made a single mistake. True or not, after two years he had still not gotten his Special Issuance Medical Certificate (SI). Whether in rehab or AA, those who continue to insist they don't have a problem are considered to be in "denial." And the wonderful thing about denial is that you can never prove it doesn't exist.

'Twelve-Step Facilitation Therapy'

If you get sucked into HIMS, "Twelve-Step Facilitation" therapy (TSF), based on AA, will become the center of your universe despite the fact that a massive literature review of studies conducted between 1966 and 2005 found that "No experimental studies unequivocally demonstrate the effectiveness of AA or TSF approaches for reducing alcohol dependence or problems."[7]

Says addiction journalist Maia Szalavitz: "At least two-thirds of abstinence-based programs—meaning virtually all treatment that isn't opioid maintenance (and some of those as well)—require [AA] meeting attendance and are based, in whole or in part, on a 12-step model, according to a survey conducted in 2009 and 2010 by the University of Georgia's National Treatment Center Study. It's fair to say that if you seek help for addiction … it's almost impossible to avoid the program, despite the fact that research shows that the 12-step model is not superior to alternatives and that most people don't stick with it."[8]

Szalavitz goes on to conclude: "… I believe that the 12 steps and indoctrination into their ideology should play *no role at all* in professional care. No one should be court-mandated or otherwise forced to attend. I also believe that it is malpractice for any professional to claim that these programs are the *only* or the *best* way to recover."[9]

Institutionalization of 'recovery dogma'

Addiction specialist Rich Jones recently wrote a piece entitled, "The Dangerous Institutionalization of Recovery Dogma," in which he described the quasi-religious intolerance applied to any addiction treatment except TSF.

According to Jones: "Things get ... problematic when state authority figures, defacto treatment experts, and perceived 'addiction medicine' experts proclaim the one way only dogma. Once the 12 step only dogma became institutionalized the public debate was over. Actually, it never got started. This model was cemented into the American psyche as the only way to recover. The dogmatic principles of 12 step recovery have been systematically reinforced over the decades."[10]

Rehabilitation centers

Rehabs abound, with some far better than others. As Richardson notes, Yelp and other sources run reviews for rehabs, which you should definitely check. HIMS will require you to spend a minimum of 28 days (more likely 30 days – or even more if your sentence ends up being extended) in whatever center your company contracts. The good news is that in HIMS, company contracts help ensure you aren't in the hands of complete quacks. The bad news is that even the best rehab centers – and the counselors they hire – have inherent conflicts of interest which may induce them to prescribe treatment you don't need. If you are re-certifying independently, you will have to find a center yourself which is thoroughly versed in FAA requirements.

As noted in Chapter 2, you will be under the complete control of the rehab to which you are remanded. You will be utterly isolated from the outside world for the first 72 hours, and your access will be severely restricted thereafter. Your personal electronic devices – phone, laptop, or tablet – will be confiscated and held until you leave.

Be nice to the nurses and aids, because they will control your life. You will eat when (and what) you are told to eat, sleep when you are told to sleep, and smoke when (and if) you are told you may. You may be restricted from soft drinks and coffee. All prescription medications will be turned in to the staff, verified, repackaged, and then dispensed at appropriate intervals (at an exorbitant fee to the contracted pharmacy, of course).

Sleeping accommodations and bathrooms may or may not be shared. Regardless, privacy will be nil since the staff can (and do) barge into your room at any time and with minimal notice, even periodically searching your possessions. (I raised hell and got a small amount of relief on that.)

Learn to love the "Big Book" of AA because even reading materials may be restricted to those relevant to recovery. Family members may visit only for a few prescribed hours, typically on weekends. Access to telephones will mean standing in line for the few installed, for which you may have to buy a long-distance phone card.

Your days in rehab will be devoted entirely to recovery. Seminars and therapy sessions – both group and individual – will start after breakfast and finish at or, more commonly, after dinner. You will be endlessly indoctrinated with slogans, including pithy selections such as "The only thing you have to change is everything." If you are truly fortunate, you will get photocopied sheets of favored slogans to facilitate better regurgitation. Get used to being told your addiction makes you "insane" and to giving the group examples of your "insanity." If you can't resist the temptation to refer to all of this as "brain-washing," be prepared to hear, "Your brain *needs* washing!"

Bring tissues. You will need them. (Just kidding. In truth, they are included in your $39,000 admission fee.) Group sessions invariably have everybody crying (at least those not too brain damaged to "share").

One joy you can count on is writing twenty or more pages (generally by hand, not computer) for the first five of the Twelve Steps of AA. You will enjoy the opportunity to read them to the group, including your most private flaws for your fourth step ("searching and fearless moral inventory") and even better, your most secret shame for your fifth step (admission "to another human being the exact nature of [your] wrongs"). But don't worry; you will get plenty of opportunities to endlessly rehash them with your counselor first.

Whatever you do, do *not* admit to harboring "resentments" about being sent to rehab (or anything else, for that matter), at least not without saying you are "working through" them. Resentment, they will insist, is the kiss of death for addicts.

You will receive relatively few options for recreation, with those available tightly controlled. Television privileges will be limited to evenings and only exercised in group rooms (none for the first 72 hours, of course). You may get the chance to join the herd for group walks, as well as periodic yoga classes and access to a workout facility.

Group outings to a beach or other recreational facility will be tightly regulated, and while on them you will be closely monitored. One popular way to avoid going stir-crazy is to go to AA meetings (where you can also get coffee and cookies generally unavailable at the rehab). My particular rehab, because it contracts with a number of airlines, also hosted meetings of "Birds of a Feather," the AA-oriented organization for pilots described below.

To give you a taste of the freedom you will enjoy, allow me to describe the day I was supposed to be released. My wife flew to the west coast to pick me up. Although I was done at 5:00 PM that day, my request to leave and spend the night with her (it had been a month, after all) was refused because my flight didn't leave until the next morning. I had to threaten to walk out to get released even a few hours before my flight home. Incidentally, had I actually walked out, it would have been "AMA" ("against medical advice"), meaning I would have received no credit for time served.

Incidentally, there are no guarantees you will be allowed to leave after 30 days. Two pilots I knew got their sentences extended, ironically by the same counselor complained about by "Scott" in the story below. By some accounts, a significant number of pilots – perhaps even a majority – get extended.

Alcoholics Anonymous

Disclaimer: As a perennial cynic and "Devil's advocate" who is profoundly uncomfortable with organized religion, I am not a good fit for AA. I despise pithy slogans, and especially "group think." If those things don't bother you, you might get along just fine.

Critics of AA abound. Beyond the sexual predators and fakes detailed in the movie *The 13th Step*, even *The Atlantic* magazine published an article entitled, "The Irrationality of Alcoholics Anonymous." Criticism tends to center either around the cult-like atmosphere of AA meetings or its downplayed but very real push for religious faith.

AA meetings are characterized by endless slogans. ("It works if you work it," "One day at a time," "Easy does it," "Let go and let God," etc.). Everyone "shares" their trials and tribulations, including their "stories" which generally involve all of the awful things done while addicted for which they now forgive themselves. You will hear endlessly about their gratitude, serenity and humility, and how they have relinquished control of their lives to God ... uh ... I mean their "higher power."

Initially, you will be told that your "higher power" may be anything to which you relinquish control (since, after all, you are powerless over alcohol and not in control of your life) and can even be AA itself. "God," you will hear, could stand for "Good Orderly Direction" or even "Group of Drunks."

But Step 2 ("Came to believe that a Power greater than ourselves could restore us to sanity"), in which you relinquish to any old "higher power" of your choosing, is only a "gateway step." (It seems a bit like idolatry to pray to AA as your "higher power," don't you think?) By Step 3, they tell you to believe not in just a "higher power" but in "God as you understand him."

Drop to your knees and pray, baby. Anything less is insufficient. God starts appearing with ever-increasing frequency as you work the steps (and your sponsor *will* demand you work the steps) until you arrive at Step 11: "Sought through prayer and meditation to improve our conscious contact with God <u>as we understood Him</u>, praying only for knowledge of His will for us and the power to carry that out."

Indeed, Step Eleven, as expanded in the book "Twelve Steps and Twelve Traditions," official literature of AA, reveals the bait-and-switch strategy when it gently chides "…certain newcomers and…those one-time agnostics who still cling to the A.A. group as their higher power…"

As far back as 1991, *Reason* magazine ran an article entitled "AA Abuse: Under the influence of alcohol –treatment evangelists, courts, employers, and parents are forcing people into 12-step programs for the slightest of reasons." The piece focused on misuse of AA in drunk-driving cases, saying: "The response to drunk driving is part of the widespread American practice of forcing or pressuring people into AA style treatment."[11]

Reason went on to recount the story of an airline pilot who was turned in by an ever-helpful fellow employee (welcome to modern corporate America) for two DUIs incurred a decade earlier. Although the piece didn't specifically discuss HIMS, it says he was forced into AA and treatment (and presumably HIMS) despite a perfect work record and a decade of sobriety.

Note: *You probably won't be told this, but a small percentage of HIMS participants choose from two lesser known abstinence-based group programs which lack AA's spiritual emphasis: SMART Recovery and Rational Recovery. One problem with them is the small number of available chapters, which might be nowhere near you. Given that you will have to attend 90 meetings in your first 90 days of recovery, and 3-4 meetings per week thereafter, it may be impossible to substitute a secular alternative.*

> **God 'as you understand him' is still God**
>
> If religion isn't your bag, in AA (and HIMS) you are pretty much S.O.L. When I was remanded back to re-education as retaliation for pointing out potential ADA violations by my company, the shrink – himself a 30-year recovering alcoholic and AA cultist – started pushing God and AA. He asked how far I had gotten in the steps, to which I responded that I was hung up on Step 11, which says: "Sought through prayer and meditation to improve our conscious contact with God as we understood Him, praying only for knowledge of His will for us and the power to carry that out." Early in AA, I noted to the shrink, they preach that anything, including the group itself, could be one's "higher power." But by Step 11, AA had me dropping to my knees and praying to God.
>
> Said the shrink: "Yes, but it says, 'God *as you understand him*.'"
>
> I responded: "Yes, but God 'as I understand him' is still God." In the interest of not provoking the shrink who would decide my fate, I refrained from pointing out that a psychiatrist in a therapeutic session should not be pushing religion.

AA is not entirely negative

Do not let me discourage you from going to AA, if it suits you. Founded in 1935, AA benefits lots of people who can't quit any other way. To its credit, it was designed for the worst alcoholics, whom the medical community of the time had failed. If I have a problem with the program (setting aside religion and group think), it is the "one-size-fits-all" approach which refuses to recognize that there are different degrees of addiction. The guy with enough self-control to confine himself to a few Martinis after work at home is not the same as the guy guzzling cough syrup while living under a bridge.

If religion doesn't bother you, AA is not necessarily as bad as critics make it out to be. In the groups I've been forced to frequent, I met a lot of nice people; people genuinely concerned about my welfare.

As a cynic and part-time misanthrope, I'm not a big believer in altruism. Even with marriages and offspring, what passes for altruism is, in fact, enlightened self-interest. That said, AA is about the closest non-familial thing to altruism I have ever encountered. Group think or not, AAs make a point of always being there to understand and to help, whatever your personal catastrophe. Yes, they teach that forgiveness and helping others is the best means of helping oneself, but at least they are upfront about it as opposed to, say, the many quacks, recovering drunks, and big-buck hustlers of the recovery industry who invariably plead, "I'm only here to help you."

> **Birds of a Feather**
>
> This is an offshoot of AA dedicated entirely to pilots. You can find chapters at www.boaf.org. The good news is that you will have lots in common with people who share your lot in life, and that by and large you will find an intelligent group with whom to "share." The bad news is that many of those at your local BOAF meetings will be the pilot collaborators of HIMS, so be very careful with what you "share." At my hometown AA, I felt free to talk about my troubles with HIMS. Not so at BOAF.

Motivations of the players

In the political organizations I direct, I teach that if you ever want to know what motivates the players in a given scenario, ask yourself what most benefits them. You will rarely be wrong.

In AA, the motivations of players are generally straightforward. They want to recover from drugs and alcohol, and they believe helping others helps them. Period. Given the honesty, AAs actually tend to be more trustworthy (at least toward fellow AAs) than the general population.

SAPs who are recovering addicts

Substance abuse professionals (SAPs) are another matter. There are good people out there, but there are also incompetents and charlatans. The problem is that in HIMS, you often don't get to pick your SAPs. And if you do get a good one, the system may decide you can no longer use them.

In terms of motivation, the many substance abuse counselors who are themselves recovering addicts are all over the map. I had three at rehab whom I deeply respected. But many of the medical professionals who are recovering addicts are also recovering incompetents. One prominent figure (and recovering co-dependent) I encountered relayed in painful detail how her alcoholic husband had repeatedly cheated on her and destroyed her life, to which she responded by ditching him and going into the field of substance abuse. As to her motivations, I can only speculate.

Most recovering addicts who become SAPs have good intentions. But it is human nature to believe others see things as you do. Although each of us experiences unique perceptions based on the myriad experiences which have shaped us, we tend to misperceive what we see as objective reality. Therefore, we believe others must see the same "truth" we do. As a psychobiology major in college, I rejected the personality theories of Sigmund Freud, Carl Jung, Alfred Adler and others as the product of flawed people who created entire personality constructs to solve their own problems, and then applied those constructs to other people. Whatever problems they had, others must too.

Similarly, SAPs who are recovering addicts remember that at their best friend's wedding, they got wasted and fell into the wedding cake. Therefore, they assume that as an addict, you must be similarly irresponsible. Everything you tell them about not having such problems will fall on deaf ears. They won't believe you and they won't care. Instead, they will say you are "in denial."

The psychiatrist who is himself (or herself) in recovery can be the biggest threat of all. Some routinely mix religion and spirituality with mental health and may be the biggest Kool-Aid drinkers you will encounter. They are living the tenets of AA, and you will too … or else. It is this species which will cheerfully destroy your career, all because they think they are "helping" you. Oh, and if you make a legitimate complaint about maltreatment at the hands of such quacks, you will be accused of "harboring resentment" which is, you will learn, a luxury recovering alcoholics cannot afford.

Allow me to relay the story of "Dr. Mike," the doctor (and recovering alcoholic) who administered HIMS for our crew base. When I had nasal surgery, I followed program guidelines precisely, reporting to my captors that I would be given high doses of Valium to sedate me for the procedure. They asked for, and I gave them, photos of the labels for the drugs prescribed.

Imagine my surprise when, three weeks later (while trying to relax on vacation, no less), I received a call from Dr. Mike saying my recent drug screen had tested positive for Serax, a drug I had never even heard of, much less used.

"Could this be a metabolite of the Valium I declared three weeks ago?" I asked.

"Absolutely not," he replied.

"Then I'm baffled," I said. "What if I can't identify the source?"

"Then you have an unexplained positive on your drug test," he said, as my past year of perfect compliance – and indeed my career – flashed before my eyes.

But a quick Internet search revealed that Serax (a.k.a. oxazepam) was indeed a metabolite of Valium (diazepam) and common in drug tests administered a few weeks following the high dose of Valium commonly administered for surgery.

"Doctor, are you aware that Serax is indeed a metabolite of Valium?" I asked.

"No, I was not."

"Would you agree that a quick glance in the *Physician's Desk Reference* could have avoided this entire debacle?"

His response was the answer of ass-covering HIMS incompetents everywhere: "Is that resentment I'm hearing?"

> **Resistance is futile; you will be assimilated**
>
> Monica Richardson's podcast, "Safe Recovery", contains an episode entitled "Airline pilot forced to attend AA meetings, forced to go to rehab sober - HIMS". It is the story of "Scott," an airline pilot who had stopped drinking but made the mistake of declaring that in the past he had used anti-depressants. Despite being sober for six months and still flying, his medical was revoked, he was forced into HIMS, and then (his second mistake) he refused to drink the Kool-Aid.
>
> Scott objected to being sent to rehab (and to its many tender mercies), to the religious aspects of both rehab and AA, and to the fact that he was called a "dry drunk" (a recovery term of art meaning that although he wasn't using alcohol or drugs, he hadn't embraced the cult of AA). As of the podcast, he had apparently been at it for two years but still didn't have his medical back. Ironically, a drug and alcohol-free assessment he obtained from an independent substance abuse professional didn't get him off the HIMS hook with the FAA … but it did disqualify him from disability insurance coverage.
>
> Ironically, he was sent to the same rehab center I was, at almost the same time, and mentioned many of the counselors and administrators I knew. Indeed, the counselor who called him a "dry drunk" was the same one who extended the stay in rehab for two pilots I knew. Scott also talked about his less-than-fond memories when he described the tactics this counselor used to intimidate patients into "acceptance." Thankfully, I had a different – and more understanding – counselor.

References:

1. L. Amato Ferri and M. Davoli, "Alcoholics Anonymous and Other 12-Step Programmes for Alcohol Dependence," *Cochrane Database Systems Review*, 3 July, 2006.
2. "The Business of Recovery: A Dose of Reality," https://www.thebusinessofrecovery.com/
3. "The Thirteenth Step", https://www.the13thstepfilm.com/
4. "Safe Recovery," https://www.blogtalkradio.com/saferecovery

5. Joe Miller, *US of AA: How the Twelve Steps Hijacked the Science of Alcoholism*, Chicago Review Press, 2019.
6. "Pleasure Unwoven," https://addictioneducationsociety.org/dr-kevin-mccauley-pleasure-unwoven/
7. Op. cit. note 1.
8. Maia Szalavitz, "What I've Finally Concluded About 12-Step Programs After 25 Years Writing About Drugs and Addiction," *Pacific Standard*, June 14, 2017, https://psmag.com/social-justice/ive-finally-concluded-12-step-programs-25-years-writing-drugs-addiction-91099
9. Ibid.
10. Richard Jones, "The Dangerous Institutionalization of Recovery Dogma," https://medium.com/@richj_87305/the-dangerous-institutionalization-of-recovery-dogma-8af9dcd67d4
11. Archie Brodsky and Stanton Peele, "A.A. Abuse: Under the influence of alcohol-treatment evangelists, courts, employers, and parents are forcing people into 12-step programs for the slightest of reasons," *Reason* magazine, November, 1991, https://staging.reason.com/1991/11/01/aa-abuse/

Chapter 5
AA, HIMS ... and Death

"If you threaten a pilot with taking away his wings, it's like threatening a doctor with taking away his stethoscope. That's a lot of leverage. If they want to get back to the cockpit or the operating room, they gotta jump through the hoops."
– Dr. Lynn Hankes, "Rehab that puts alcoholic pilots back in the cockpit"[1]

The dirty little secret of the HIMS program is that, at least in some cases, the non-scientific approach on which it is based may be killing people. The elevated death rate of practicing alcoholics is well established. What is less often realized is that the death rate of *recovered* alcoholics does not significantly decline. (The rates are 3.6 and 2.9 times that of the non-alcoholic population, respectively.[2])

AA is notoriously ineffective

For starters, HIMS is utterly dependent on AA, a notoriously non-scientific and spiritually-based recovery program dating from the relative dark ages of 1935. Although the anonymity of AA participants makes it impossible to debunk AA's claimed recovery rate of 75 percent (of those who "really tried," according to AA's "Big Book"), independent research suggests its success rate is more on the order of 5-8 percent.[3]

Lance Dodes, MD and Zachary Dodes, coauthors of *The Sober Truth: Debunking the Bad Science Behind 12-Step Programs and the Rehab Industry*, open the book by saying: "Alcoholics Anonymous was proclaimed the correct treatment for alcoholism over seventy-five years ago despite the absence of any scientific evidence of the approach's efficacy, and we have been on the wrong path ever since."[4]

An extensive article in *The Atlantic* magazine entitled "The Irrationality of Alcoholics Anonymous" notes that "Nowhere in the field of medicine is treatment less grounded in modern science." It also notes, "... nothing about the 12-step approach draws on modern science: not the character building, not the tough love, not even the standard 28-day rehab stay." The article goes on to point out that in *The Handbook of Alcoholism Treatment Approaches*, AA ranks 38 out of the 48 approaches evaluated.[5] *The Atlantic* piece also criticizes AA's "one size fits all" approach to substance abuse treatment, noting that the program was originally intended for chronic, severe alcoholics but is now being applied to those with far milder disorders.

Regardless, you won't get far criticizing AA. In her article entitled "After 75 Years of Alcoholics Anonymous, It's Time to Admit We Have a Problem," addiction journalist Maia Szalavitz says: "For much of the past 50 years or so, voicing any serious skepticism toward Alcoholics Anonymous or any other 12-step program was sacrilege—the equivalent, in polite company, of questioning the virtue of American mothers or the patriotism of our troops."[6]

Szalavitz, who wrote *Unbroken Brain: A Revolutionary New Way of Understanding Addiction*[7], which hypothesizes that addiction is a developmental disorder, describes the irrationality of Twelve-Step Facilitation therapy (TSF):

> "... if you take a look at the 12 steps themselves, it's easy to see why this form of therapy is unlike any other. The first step requires an admission of 'powerlessness' over the addiction, the second a belief in a 'Higher Power' that can restore you to 'sanity,' the third a surrender to 'God as we understood Him.'
>
> "Steps 4 through 10 involve taking a moral inventory and publicly confessing it to someone, asking God to remove your 'defects of character,' then making amends for harm done.

"If such steps were demanded of people in treatment for any other condition, they would very likely argue that they were being treated as sinners rather than patients. Would you choose a psychiatrist who wanted to focus on your moral failings rather than your medical condition?"[8]

Dodes reinforces the point that AA dogma is founded in neither science nor effectiveness: "AA's emphasis on proselytizing, a basic tool through which recognized religions and certain fringe religious groups spread their message, is an essential part of its worldwide success, and it's a big reason that it has been nearly impossible to have an open national dialogue about other, potentially better ways to treat addiction."[9]

Finally, it is taken on faith – both in AA and TSF recovery programs – that left untreated, addiction to alcohol will inevitably kill you. As "evidence," you will hear about all sorts of people who left the program and promptly died. But that too is an exaggeration. Ignoring for a moment that anecdotes rarely tell you *how* they die (suicide after having their personalities ripped out in TSF, perhaps?), even E. Morton Jellinek, developer of the disease model for alcoholism, eventually disavowed his own "Jellinek Curve" – the theory of "inevitable deterioration" of the disease. Regardless, as a tenet of its "one-size-fits-most" philosophy, AA continues to claim the long-discredited "inevitability" of Death by Alcoholism.[10]

One alternative to abstinence-based treatment

As documented by John David Sinclair, a doctor treating alcohol dependence in Finland, abstinence-based programs produce "deprivation effect" wherein abstinence actually increases binge-drinking whenever alcohol consumption is resumed. AA is fond of saying that while you are abstinent, "Your disease is doing pushups." What TSF apologists fail to mention is that AA is the one acting as "personal trainer" for the disease.

Sinclair and others found that opioid antagonists such as naltrexone blocked endorphins from reaching opiate receptors in the brain, reducing the number of responsible neural synapses and therefore alcohol cravings. In 2001 Sinclair's paper in the journal *Alcohol and Alcoholism* reported that 78 percent of patients reduced drinking to about 10 drinks per week.

Sinclair himself says: "The Sinclair Method was confirmed, first in a large body of laboratory studies, then in over 90 clinical trials around the world, and most recently in personal reports by people using. It has been found to be successful in about 80% of alcoholics."[11]

According to the "C Three (C^3) Foundation,"[12] which is the primary advocate for The Sinclair Method:

> *"The Sinclair Method (TSM) is a treatment for alcohol addiction that uses a technique called pharmacological extinction — the use of an opiate blocker to turn habit-forming behaviors into habit-erasing behaviors. The effect returns a person's craving for alcohol to its pre-addiction state.*
>
> *"TSM consists of taking Naltrexone or Nalmefene one hour before your first drink of the day for the rest of your life as long as you continue to drink. Naltrexone (or Nalmefene) chemically disrupts the body's behavior/reward cycle causing you to want to drink less instead of more."*

Of course, the chances of the FAA approving the use of Naltrexone while flying remain, shall we say, somewhat limited. When HIMS was conceived in 1973, AA might have been the only game in town. But while recent advances in behavioral genetics and psychopharmacology have left AA and TSF behind, HIMS continues to cling to outmoded treatments which may actually harm participants.

AA is not all bad...

As noted earlier, I'm not saying that nobody should use AA. Momentarily ignoring the myths on which AA is based, even Dodes notes the benefits of "group dynamics" in helping alcoholics recover. According to another study: "Meetings provide an opportunity to share one's own struggles... increase one's motivation to abstain, and ... get outside of one's self... by hearing others talk about their problems."[13]

But how about HIMS?

HIMS claims a far higher success rate than AA, alleging that 90 percent[14] of pilots treated "recover." Before celebrating the effectiveness of HIMS, however, understand that the difference likely results from "compliance bias." Ignoring for a moment that the figure dates from 1984, and that I was unable to find underlying data for the claim, even if it is true, there are three significant differences between the HIMS population and those who merely participate in AA:

1. **Airline pilots are more motivated and professional than the population at large:** Whether from the military or civilian sector, pilots are success-oriented individuals by nature. Moreover, they have invested years and often tens of thousands of dollars to build a career in which their skills do not translate to other jobs, making them highly motivated to regain those careers.

2. **Monitoring and scrutiny are far greater than for AA:** For better or worse, unlike in AA, if you cheat in HIMS, you will almost certainly get caught. Routine substance use monitoring keeps people honest.

3. **The monetary threat to a pilot's career is far greater than for most people:** As I said to the Las Vegas Uber driver who repeatedly tried to steer me to a happy hour bar: "How much would that drink cost you?"

He answered, "I dunno, about 5 bucks?"

I responded, "Well, that same drink would cost me about $300,000. Do you think it's worth it?"

> **Meet 'compliance bias'**
>
> Lance Dodes, M.D., is a Training and Supervising Analyst Emeritus with the Boston Psychoanalytic Society and Institute and retired as an assistant clinical professor of psychiatry at Harvard Medical School. He has been the Director of the substance abuse treatment unit of Harvard's McLean Hospital, Director of the Alcoholism Treatment Unit at Spaulding Rehabilitation Hospital, and Director of the Boston Center for Problem Gambling.
>
> Here is what Dodes has to say about the "success" of certain groups in AA: "This kind of problem with evidence is so well-known that it has its own name: 'compliance bias.' It is just this bias that is common in addiction research, where people who become invested in (comply) with any given treatment regularly do better than can be expected from the general population."[15]

How's that 'recovery' working for you?

"Recovery" in abstinence-based programs does not typically equate to mental health, even for those who succeed. Recovered alcoholics frequently report:

- Depression
- Anxiety
- Psychosis
- Hostility
- Feelings of inadequacy
- Paranoia
- Phobias

The shrink my company sent me to expressed concern about my continued abstinence after my retirement, noting that many of his patients died due to alcohol within two years after retiring. I pointed out that my health after retirement was not his concern, and that our interaction should focus only on my fitness to fly. Had I been less kind, I might also have pointed out that binge behavior actually increases in abstinence-based programs, so it was entirely possible that his outdated mode of treatment might actually contribute to the mortality rate of his patients.

Suicide?

The question nobody seems to want to deal with is whether HIMS actually increases suicide rates among participants. As noted earlier, we certainly had more than our share in the HIMS group for just my crew base. Extrapolating to multiple airlines and crew base, one might speculate 100 or more HIMS-related suicides per year.

Even outside HIMS, one in four deaths among **treated** alcoholics results from suicide.[16] Given that pilots tend to be "Type A" personalities driven to succeed; that they may be aggravated by AA's attempt to re-engineer their personalities through group think and superficial slogans ("The only thing you need to change is everything!"); and that HIMS administrators stand ready to end careers of pilots who fail to toe the line, one might expect some pilots to conclude they had "failed" to sufficiently re-engineer their personalities. The result might well be suicide.

In the same vein, treatment failure is often blamed on patients. "It works if you work it," goes the slogan. If it doesn't, you "aren't ready to stay sober," they will insist, or you "haven't reached bottom yet." Underlying any relapse or slip is the presumption that *you* aren't "working it" hard enough.

Indeed, AA regards inability to quit as a character flaw, saying in the "Big Book":

> *"Rarely have we seen a person fail who has thoroughly followed our path. Those who do not recover are people who cannot or will not completely give themselves to this simple program, usually men and women who are constitutionally incapable of being hon-*

> *est with themselves. There are such unfortunates. They are not at fault; they seem to have been born that way."*

Translated, if you relapse, the program didn't fail, **you did**. Add to that the success-oriented personality type drawn to professional aviation and the result of "failure" becomes sadly predictable.

Then, of course, we have the impact of the program on a pilot's relationships, a potential disaster HIMS both acknowledges and accepts. As himsprogram.com says: "The nature of the relationship with the pilot's spouse will be completely transformed or may end."[17] Maybe you're comfortable with that; I wasn't. And yes, I met many pilots in the throes of divorce which occurred *after* they began treatment.

Speaking personally, I am quite happy to have re-established my pre-recovery persona. My strength of will and relatively organized approach to problem-solving have enabled me to accomplish much. But "Captain Asshole" didn't appeal to my overseers, who denounced willpower and demanded that I accept my "powerlessness" while surrendering my life to God. Had I actually tried (and inevitably failed) to comply with their demands, I probably wouldn't be around to write this book.

Is AA a religious cult?

"Alcoholics Anonymous has an official party line that says you have complete freedom of religion, and you can belong to any religion you wish, or you can have no religion at all. [In truth,] AA members will make every effort to convert you to the official AA religious beliefs..." So begins an enlightening site called "The Orange Papers."

Although the FAA does not officially require AA, in practice you have few other options, as secular 12-step programs are few and far between. You will be told you don't have to believe in God, just "God as you understand him;" you will hear that your "higher power" can be anything you like including AA itself (at least for the first step). "God," they will say, can stand for "Good Orderly Direction."

But make no mistake: "God as you understand him" is still God. The Seventh Circuit Court of Appeals in Kerr vs. Farrey stated: "A straightforward reading of the twelve steps shows clearly that the steps are based on the monotheistic idea of a single God or Supreme Being."

"AA Agnostica" (https://aaagnostica.org/2012/05/27/the-courts-aa-and-religion/) does an excellent analysis of judicial scrutiny of AA with respect to the "Establishment Clause" of the First Amendment ("Congress shall make no law respecting an establishment of religion").

According to the Supreme Court (Everson v. Board of Education): *"... [t]he 'establishment of religion' clause of the First Amendment means at least this: Neither a state nor the Federal Government ... can pass laws which aid one religion, aid all religions, or prefer one religion over another. Neither can force nor influence a person to go to or to remain away from church against his will or force him to profess a belief or disbelief in any religion. No person can be punished for entertaining or professing religious beliefs or disbeliefs, for church attendance or nonattendance ... Neither a state nor the Federal Government can, openly or secretly, participate in the affairs of any religious organizations or groups and vice versa."*

Five high-level courts (and numerous lower courts) have held that AA is essentially a religious organization, and that forced participation violates the Establishment Clause: Griffin v. Coughlin (1996), Kerr v. Farrey (1996), Arnold & Evans v. Tennessee Board of Paroles (1997), Warner v. Orange County Dept. of Probation (1999), and Inouye v. Kemna (2007).

References:

1. "Rehab that puts alcoholic pilots back in the cockpit," *CBS News*, December 10, 2017, https://www.cbsnews.com/news/rehab-that-puts-alcoholic-pilots-back-in-the-cockpit/
2. Health Recovery Center, "The Best Kept Secret," http://joanmathewslarson.com/HRC_2006/BestSecret.htm
3. Lance Dodes, MD and Zachary Dodes, *The Sober Truth: Debunking the Bad Science Behind 12-Step Programs and the Rehab Industry*, Beacon Press, 2014.
4. Op. cit. note 2.
5. Gabrielle Glaser, "The Irrationality of Alcoholics Anonymous," *The Atlantic*, April, 2015: https://www.theatlantic.com/magazine/archive/2015/04/the-irrationality-of-alcoholics-anonymous/386255/
6. Maia Szalavitz, "After 75 Years of Alcoholics Anonymous, It's Time to Admit We Have a Problem," *Pacific Standard*, https://psmag.com/social-justice/75-years-alcoholics-anonymous-time-admit-problem-74268
7. Maia Svalavitz, *Unbroken Brain: A Revolutionary New Way of Understanding Addiction*, Picador, 2016.
8. Maia Svalavitz, "Does Addiction Treatment Require A Higher Power?," *National Public Radio*, May 1, 2016, https://www.npr.org/sections/health-shots/2016/05/01/476193634/does-addiction-treatment-require-a-higher-power
9. Op. cit. note 3.
10. Op. cit. note 2.
11. "Definitive statement" by John David Sinclair, PhD, C^3 Foundation, https://cthreefoundation.org/resources/definitive-statement-by-john-david-sinclair-ph-d
12. C^3 Foundation, https://cthreefoundation.org/the-sinclair-method
13. L. Kaskutas, "Alcoholics Anonymous Effectiveness: Faith Meets Science," *Journal of Addictive Diseases* 28, no. 2 (2009): 145-157, https://www.ncbi.nlm.nih.gov/pmc/articles/PMC2746426/
14. "HIMS: A Restoring Force," http://himsprogram.com/Content/HimsResources/RestoringForce.htm
15. Lance Dodes, MD, "What do we really know about addiction?", *The Fix*, June 4, 2015, https://www.thefix.com/content/what-do-we-really-know-about-addiction-lance-dodes0604
16. Op. cit. note 1.
17. "Aftercare / Monitoring," http://www.himsprogram.com/Content/Aftercare

Chapter 6
Navigating HIMS: Up to Your 'SI'

Disclaimer: I am neither a lawyer nor a substance abuse professional. Nothing herein should be construed as legal or medical advice. For drug and alcohol addiction issues, I strongly recommend you remove yourself from flying immediately and contact a substance abuse professional. For Federal Aviation Administration (FAA) compliance questions, contact a qualified attorney.

How you might end up in HIMS

Not all who lose medical certificates over substance abuse or end up in HIMS have flown drunk, had a DOT positive test or a DUI, or have been convicted of alcohol or drug-related offenses. Many are reported by other people, often for the most capricious (or malicious) reasons. As previously noted, I was reported after an argument with a hotel security guard. I've met others reported by a vindictive ex-wife or by a customer service agent who happened to see a captain limp (from a chronic knee injury). A remarkable number of naïve individuals even self-admit, usually to their eventual regret.

Once in the path of the HIMS tornado, don't think for a moment that the fact you aren't addicted will enable you to escape its vortex. As noted previously, even an assessment from an independent substance abuse professional (SAP) likely won't get you off the hook with HIMS.

What if you get a DUI?

Given increasingly stringent DUI enforcement, this is undoubtedly the most common funnel into HIMS. In the early 2000s, the FAA began scrutinizing each DUI *charge* (not just conviction), changing their long-standing policy that a single DUI would not disqualify you from holding a medical certificate.

For any drug or alcohol-related offense or if you are charged with operating a motor vehicle (including boats) under the influence, you must report twice:

1. Under FAR 61.15, you must report any DUI within 60 days upon penalty of suspension of airman and medical certificates. You must report it to the FAA Security and Investigations Division.

2. You must report the incident (convictions as well as arrests and administrative actions) on your next FAA medical examination by checking "yes" in question 18v of FAA Form 8500-8. This would include any license revocations, reductions of charges or dismissals. The FAA will require police and court records, together with a letter of explanation, which they will review with an eye for patterns of behavior.[1]

Check with the FAA for specifics of DUI reporting requirements.[2] You can also find general information at barnettlegal.com and from the FAA's "Alcohol and Flying" brochure.[3]

A blood alcohol concentration (BAC) of 0.15 or higher will require a formal substance abuse evaluation, probably from a HIMS AME (Aeromedical Examiner).[4] Consult with an AME long before your medical expires to prevent interruption of your privileges.

With a BAC of 0.20 or more, you are in deep doo-doo. The FAA will likely conclude substance dependence, require psychiatric and psychological evaluations, and remand you to the HIMS process (whether or not you have access to an organized HIMS program). You will likely need to work the system to qualify for a Special Issuance Medical Certificate (SI).

Lawyers might advise you to refuse a sobriety test during a DUI traffic stop in order to deny the prosecution evidence, but doing so will probably make you end up in HIMS too. As noted elsewhere, I met one HIMS participant there by virtue of refusing a sobriety test. He also made the mistake of insisting he was not an alcoholic. When I spoke to him, he had been in the program for two years and still didn't have a SI.

Antidepressants

Here too things have changed in recent years. Following transient use of antidepressants for a single episode of depression, you can apply for a regular medical certificate in 90 days with a doctor's statement that you no longer need the drug.

Long-term use of anti-depressants is more problematic and depends on the severity of depression and the type of SSRI (selective serotonin reuptake inhibitor) drug used. Consult an AME for details.

When the HIMS EF5 tornado bears down on you

The moment you discover that somebody wants you in HIMS, stop drinking immediately. (Note: If you are a hardcore alcoholic, a substance abuse professional would likely tell you not to quit drinking without consulting a physician. Untreated alcohol withdrawal could kill you.) You will likely be headed for a PEth test, which may detect even a single episode of so-called "binge-drinking" for twelve days or more and multiple episodes for a month or more.

I strongly urge you to seek counsel from a lawyer (and preferably more than one lawyer) who deals regularly with FAA medical and HIMS issues. Do not rely solely on legal advice provided by a union. If you are a union member, contact your local representative but don't necessarily expect much sympathy. Also, don't blindly follow the advice of the ever-helpful pilot representatives in HIMS, who are themselves recovering and who will probably regard it as their mission to suck as many pilots as possible into their little utopia of serenity, acceptance, powerlessness and gratitude.

If I had it to do over, I would not volunteer for anything. My union representatives claimed I would be better off volunteering for an evaluation with a union-recommended psychiatrist instead of one provided by the company. In truth, because a diagnosis of alcohol or substance abuse disorder is pretty much the same whoever renders it, using a union-recommended psychiatrist may confer few, if any, advantages. If the outcome of a PEth test might be in doubt, one might consider forcing the company to go through all of the contractual steps short of termination, which could protract the process for a month or more (while abstaining from alcohol and mood-altering substances, or course).

Incidentally, if you think you might have a problem yet manage to escape the clutches of the FAA and HIMS regardless, I strongly suggest you seek help from a SAP and/or AA, SMART Recovery or an equivalent program.

What is HIMS?

The "Human Intervention Motivation Study" began in 1973, prior to which aviators diagnosed with alcoholism or drug abuse rarely returned to the cockpit. Intended to provide pilots a means of regaining FAA medical certificates, it was, in fairness, based on what was arguably the best treatment of its time.

Understand that HIMS is largely an "old boy network" and, as such, is not neatly defined. You are dealing with a program developed nearly five decades ago which has not fundamentally changed since. Rather than being based on objective standards and empirically-derived methods, it is the embodiment of cult-based AA and a network of bureaucrats who mutually justify each other's existence. At this point, the HIMS program itself is little more than a cult built on failed twelve-step facilitation therapy (TSF) which is sanctioned by the FAA and abused by airlines to circumvent labor protections and artificially increase the productivity of pilots.

If, for example, you ask for a published list of HIMS-certified psychiatrists, you will learn it doesn't exist (psychologists, yes, but not psychiatrists), or so I was told by personnel at the FAA aeromedical branch in

Oklahoma City who, when pressed, gave me the phone number for the office of the FAA's head psychiatrist. When I called that office, they not only failed to give me a list of HIMS-certified psychiatrists, but indignantly demanded: "Who gave you this number?"

While HIMS bureaucrats claim high levels of success in restoring pilots' careers, the confounding variables inherent in their claims are:

1. HIMS deals exclusively with intelligent, motivated participants;
2. Participants who fail are threatened with a great loss (i.e. their careers); and
3. Participants are closely monitored, such that "cheating" is virtually impossible.

Those differences may explain why HIMS claims to have a 90 percent success rate, while studies have found only about a five to ten percent success rate for the AA program which underpins it.

Going it alone?

HIMS was conceived to facilitate recertification of professional pilots. Expedited return to the flight deck involves oversight by peers, supervisors and substance abuse professionals, as well as the FAA. Pilots not subject to HIMS (typically pilots not flying under FAR Part 121) are required to recertify by other means, including finding an IMS (Independent Medical Sponsor) to navigate FAA recertification, typically the two-year process stipulated by FAR 67.107.

That said, because recertification is managed on a case-by-case basis, there is considerable variation in requirements when recertifying independently. Many aviators work with HIMS-certified IMSs, and I have even met a helicopter pilot whose company didn't have HIMS and who was working a sort of "parallel HIMS" program using a major airline's IMS. Given the variability in recertification programs, you should select your IMS with great care. See the FAA's guide to recertification monitoring.[5]

In fairness to organized HIMS programs, independently compiling the necessary documentation for FAA medical recertification during substance dependence recovery is a daunting task. Professional pilots I have met who were doing it themselves had thick binders of documentation to show for their efforts. Additional information is available from the Aircraft Owners and Pilots Association (AOPA) at the website listed in references below.[6]

The HIMS process

For a sanitized and somewhat optimistic version of necessary steps in the HIMS program, check himsprogram.com/Content/ReCert. For a more realistic overview, see Appendix C. Other resources are listed at the end of this chapter.

I will say this repeatedly throughout this book: ***Document everything***. Keep phone logs or records of every call, conversation, meeting, letter, email, drug/alcohol testing notification and result, or other action, whether by you or others. If you can legally do so (i.e. if you are operating in a "one-party consent" state in which you can record conversations to which you are a party), consider recording phone calls and meetings. (Caveat: Just because recording is legal does not mean it is permissible by your company's policies.)

Substance abuse/dependence evaluation

Generally conducted by a psychiatrist specializing in substance abuse, you can expect an extraordinarily thorough interview followed by a blood test. A Google search on "what to expect at a substance abuse evaluation" should give you an idea of what screening and assessment will look like.

If your company has a HIMS program, they will direct you to the appropriate SAP. If you are a recertifying independently or your employer doesn't have HIMS, finding a SAP who can complete the evaluation is more complicated, since not any psychiatrist will do. To quote the FAA:

"Who may perform a psychiatric evaluation? Psychiatric evaluations must be conducted by a qualified psychiatrist who is board-certified by the American Board of Psychiatry and Neurology or the American Board of Osteopathic Neurology and Psychiatry, and must either be board certified in Addiction Psychiatry or have received training in the Human Intervention Motivation Study (HIMS) program. Preference is given for those who have completed HIMS training. Using a psychiatrist without this background may limit the usefulness of the report."[7]

Interview

We should note that the FAA criteria for substance abuse/dependence do not currently align with the American Psychiatric Association's *Diagnostic and Statistical Manual of Mental Disorders* (DSM–5). In general (not specifically FAA requirements), substance abuse initial screening may include the CAGE Questionnaire,[8] Alcohol Use Inventory (AUDIT),[9] and Substance Abuse Subtle Screening Inventory (SASSI).[10] Assessment in greater depth may include the Diagnostic Interview Schedule-IV (DIS-IV)[11] and Addiction Severity Index (ASI),[12] and may involve contacting family or friends. In my case, the psychiatrist asked to call my wife.

Expect a two-hour assessment including:

- Your family, including your relationships with them and any substance abuse experienced by others
- Any brushes you might ever had with the law, whether or not related to substance abuse
- Your full medical history, including prescription medications used
- Your mental health history
- Your finances
- Any time back to the womb when you might ever have used a mood-altering chemical (for example, my FAA file now contains the ever-so-revealing statistic that the sommelier of the renowned Four Seasons restaurant in New York tasked me with wine tasting at age five … in 1964)

❏ Your use of mood-altering substances, including questions like:

- When did you begin using alcohol or drugs?
- What do you use?
- How much do you use?
- Has anyone ever suggested you quit or cut back?
- Has using affected your reputation?
- Have you made promises to control using and then broken them?
- Have you ever changed patterns in an effort to control consumption?
- Have you ever gotten into financial, legal, or marital difficulties?
- Have you ever lost time from work because of using or drinking?
- Have you ever sneaked or hidden your use?
- Do you sometimes feel uncomfortable if alcohol or your drug is not available?
- Do you continue drinking or using when friends or family suggest you have had enough?
- Have you ever felt remorse about your drinking or using or what you did while under the influence?
- Has your efficiency decreased as a result of your drinking or using?
- When using or drinking, do you neglect to eat properly?
- Do you use or drink alone?
- Are you in a hurry to finish your first drink?
- Do you use or drink more than usual when under pressure, angry, or depressed?
- Are you able to drink or use more now without feeling it, compared to when you first started using?
- Have you lost interest in other activities or noticed a decrease in ambition due to drinking or using?
- Have you had the shakes or tremors following heavy drinking or using or not using for a period of time?
- Do you want to drink or use at a particular time each day?

- Do you drink more than four drinks per day and feel ill at ease when you don't?
- Do you go on and off the wagon?
- Is drinking or using jeopardizing your job?
- Do you ever start out to just have two or three drinks and get drunk when you do not intend to?
- Do you find that you cannot predict how much you will drink after your first drink on a social occasion?
- Do you ever promise yourself you'll stop drinking or slow down and then break that promise?
- Do you drink more heavily when you are under pressure or after a disappointment or quarrel?
- Do you require a drink the next morning to calm your nerves?
- Have you had more than one bender in the past six months?
- Do you use tranquilizers during periods of time when you are unwilling or unable to drink alcohol?

Substance abuse testing

Expect a PEth test, which tests for long-term metabolites of alcohol in the blood. For details on PEth testing, check Chapter 7.

So you failed the test...

If you fail the assessment, indicating (at least to the powers that be) that you suffer from some level of "alcohol use disorder" (AUD), you face essentially four options:

1. **Stop flying:** Upon a diagnosis of alcohol or drug dependence, your medical certificate becomes null and void. Only through the protracted HIMS process or some variant – either through an organized HIMS program or through an Independent Medical Sponsor (IMS) – can you restore your FAA medical privileges through a Special Issuance medical certificate (SI).

2. **Recertify independently:** There are HIMS AMEs not associated with airlines who will claim to have your SI in a matter of months, and who will recommend 28-day inpatient treatment programs and otherwise guide you ... for a fee. That fee might be overt, or it might be in the form of kickbacks from the inpatient treatment program they recommend. As noted elsewhere, recertifying independently is a Herculean task, requiring you to become intimately familiar with the FAA's many arcane requirements and keeping reams of documentation. Figure on two years to get your medical back per FAR 67.107. Even if you get your medical back independently, your airline might not take you back without HIMS.

3. **Embrace HIMS:** The good news is that your ever-helpful HIMS "brothers" will whisk you off to rehab and start you through a program that most participants don't fully comprehend. Everything will be handled for you, at least initially. The bad news is that for the price of simplicity and economy, you pay dearly in lifestyle, regimentation, and psychological pain, probably for five or more years.

4. **Fight:** A fourth option might be to use the lawyer you consulted earlier to fight for your medical and avoid the assessment altogether. In this layman's opinion, after a diagnosis of AUD, your chances of success will be greatly diminished. That said, however, I have seen at least one pilot use legal representation and guile after getting a DUI to avoid HIMS, so it *can* be done. If you choose this option, you need to be ready for the battle of your life.

Signing your life away ... literally

So now you are contemplating the end of your career – everything you have invested, potentially, gone in smoke. Maybe you also face the loss of income, your home, your kids' education, perhaps your marriage. It is at this point of extreme emotional distress that the thoughtful pilot collaborators and HIMS bureaucrats will hand you the key to your "salvation," the HIMS agreement.

"Sign it and we will help you save your life," they will insist. "It is entirely at your discretion, of course." If you don't want to consent, feel free not to sign it ... and lose your career.

What they will not say is that signing the HIMS agreement could also help them *end* your life, at least as you know it, and perhaps literally. It is what gives them the authority to require whatever course of treatment they choose, including lots of options which to you, the unwashed, bear no apparent relationship to substance dependence.

For example, if you object to their tender mercies, the HIMS agreement lets them send you to an "anger management" counselor or, better yet, to a psychiatrist who has the option – or in at least one well-documented case of malfeasance, the pre-ordained, bought-and-paid-for task – of diagnosing you with a mental disorder.

Whether or not the psychiatrist is acting as a rubber stamp for your company, understand two things: First, the psychiatrist they recommend will be part of a close-knit network of FAA cronies who will be loath to contradict the HIMS bureaucrats who sent you. Second, being branded with mental illness or a personality disorder will haunt you not only with FAA medical certification, but in all aspects of your life.

But hey, signing the HIMS agreement is your choice, right?

Inpatient treatment

Welcome to the joys of rehab. Chapter 4 details what you can expect from inpatient treatment, so I won't belabor it here. Suffice to say you are destined for 28-30 days of isolated sobriety boot camp in which independent thinking will earn you a lengthened sentence.

The first step of inpatient treatment is detoxification, the duration of which can vary with level of alcohol or drug dependence. Because alcohol, unlike some other drugs, penetrates the "blood-brain barrier," creating potentially dangerous withdrawal symptoms, you will be advised not to quit drinking before arriving at rehab. To ease withdrawal, patients are often given benzodiazepines.

Residential treatment facility requirements:[13, 14]

With rare exceptions, after a diagnosis of substance dependence, getting an SI will require attending a 28-day (or more) residential treatment program. Exceptions might include a diagnosis of mild or moderate conditions, but those will be decided on a case-by-case basis. With few exceptions, air carrier pilots operating under FAR Part 121 can expect to be required to complete residential treatment.

Although there is no specific list of HIMS-approved treatment facilities, the complexities of FAA medical re-certification virtually mandate using a facility with extensive experience in treating pilots and dealing with FAA requirements. Using such facilities will result in better treatment outcomes and fewer delays in recertification.

Top 10 residential facility characteristics to look for:

- Full-time, certified addiction specialist physician on staff
- Credentialed/certified counselors (generally with some in recovery)
- Acceptance of the disease model of addiction
- Abstinence-based treatment
- Dedicated substance abuse program (apart from psychiatric patients)
- Psychiatry and psychology consultants
- Family involvement in treatment
- AA 12-step-based recovery program (yes, AA or NA, despite lip service paid to alternatives)
- Accreditation and/or licensure agency endorsements
- Facility works frequently with HIMS and has HIMS-oriented preparation and discharge planning

Cognitive testing:

One thing not previously mentioned is that prior to release from inpatient treatment, you will be tested for loss of cognitive abilities which might result from substance abuse. This testing will give a baseline and is a precursor to and preparation for the "P&P" (Psychiatric and Psychological Evaluations), which are a required part of your application package for your SI.

The primary tool for the assessment may be the "CogScreen-AE,"[15] which will measure attention; working memory; focus; visual perception speed; information processing speed; language; letter sequencing; reading comprehension; executive function; logical problem solving; math knowledge, speed and fluency; memory; information processing speed; visual scanning; reaction time and more. Potential impairment will be estimated by comparing your performance to that of other aviators and to the general population, corrected for age and education. For a layman's overview of what you will experience, check www.pilotsofamerica.com/community/threads/cogscreen.108790/ and also www.cogscreen.com/Overview.aspx.

Outpatient treatment[16]

Your "Independent Medical Sponsor" and you

At some point, probably prior to rehab, you will select an "Independent Medical Sponsor" (IMS), who is a specially trained HIMS Aviation Medical Examiner (AME) and who will be your representative to the FAA, including:

❏ Reviewing and compiling necessary records
❏ Having regular meetings (probably monthly) with you
❏ Monitoring or conducting regular abstinence testing

If you are in an organized HIMS program for an airline, they will have an IMS in the program. If you are not in an airline HIMS program, the IMS could charge $1000-$2000 per year.

HIMS meetings—the nightmare union of recovery & corporate discipline

Once out of rehab, you will be assigned a peer monitor, typically another pilot in the HIMS program to whom you will be required to periodically report.

You will also be required to attend monthly HIMS monitoring meetings, which typically comprise a representative from your chief pilot's office, HIMS personnel (e.g. Employee Assistance Program and a contractor, if your airline employs one), the IMS (or his or her representatives), and you.

Depending on your airline, if any, these meetings might seem similar to AA meetings, but rest assured they are not. At an AA meeting, you are *encouraged* to "share" your story; at HIMS meetings, you are *required* to share. Unlike, AA, there is no anonymity at a HIMS meeting. Instead of identifying your "shares" by saying, "I'm Joe and I'm an alcoholic," at a HIMS meeting, you will say, "I'm Joe *Smith*, and I'm an alcoholic," and your overseers will be busy writing down everything you say to ensure you are being sufficiently supplicant.

Depending on your airline's approved program, a question regarding recovery may be posed to the group, and each pilot will be required to answer. Carefully consider your response, since saying the wrong thing could easily place you into "re-evaluation" for anything the psychiatrist might construe as "anger," "resentment," or "denial." Remember that your *SI can be yanked if any single entity, including the chief pilot, is not happy with you.*

After getting my SI and flying the line for a year, I attended a HIMS monitoring meeting at which we were asked how we were doing with our (non-existent) "anonymity." I replied that I valued my anonymity and was therefore shocked when a representative of the chief pilot's office "outed" me in a company meeting to people who had no idea I was in HIMS. Back to the shrink for me, since I was apparently having "anger management" issues.

Remember what I said about psychiatrists being the biggest threat to your career when they themselves are in recovery? (See Chapter 4.) For years I have joked that the mental health trap has become so all-encompassing that "does not play well with other children" is probably a diagnosis in the *Diagnostic and Statistical Manual of Mental Disorders*. Well, in the lovely tête-à-tête with the shrink, which resulted from my comments at the HIMS meeting, I learned my joke is no longer funny because it is true; "does not play well with other children" is now "narcissistic personality disorder," and if the ever-helpful Dr. Recovering Alcoholic levies it at you, your career might be over.

To summarize, it is primarily at the HIMS monitoring meeting that the nightmare union of recovery and discipline occurs. Make no mistake: ***you are entirely the creature of your company, which can use HIMS to end your career at any time***.

The first 90 days

Your first 90 days out of rehab will be busy, and will likely include:

- **Intensive Outpatient therapy (IOP)**: You will probably attend three group sessions per week comprising three hours per session for 90 days.

- **90 AA meetings in 90 days**: You will have to document the AA meetings and, in general, you may not "stack" meetings (e.g. doing three meetings in one day and none for the next two days) except where absolutely necessary. After 90 days, you will still be required to attend AA meetings at a rate prescribed by the psychiatrist (probably a minimum of three per week). You will be strongly encouraged to get an AA "sponsor," who will likely require you to work the steps of the AA program.

- **Intensive alcohol monitoring:** For at least the first 90 days, you will likely be issued a Soberlink®[17] device, a remote breathalyzer which transmits results electronically. You will be required to blow into it every four hours of your waking existence. If you think you can fool the device, think again. Nobody else can blow into it for you; it takes your picture, which it subjects to facial recognition software. It will go everywhere you do, and you will have to leave dinner parties, sports events or whatever else you attend in order to blow into it every four hours. If you fail to do so, expect a call from HIMS personnel. After 90 days, you may "graduate" to "random" urine testing (it isn't really random) 14 times per year, which you will do by going to an approved testing site when summoned. (I have, however, heard of at least one airline which uses Soberlink® for the entire duration of the SI.) Depending on your airline, you may have to bear some or all of the cost of testing.

Continuing aftercare

Beyond the first 90 days, up until applying for your SI, you will be required to:

- Continue going to AA meetings, including working the steps, three or more times per week
- Attend HIMS monitoring meetings, typically one per month
- Attend group aftercare (which is different in content and structure from IOP), typically four per month
- Periodically check in with your peer monitor, typically once per week
- Continue drug and alcohol monitoring via random urine (and occasional blood) testing 14 times per year
- Whatever else your HIMS overseers mandate (e.g. anger management counseling, etc.)

This monitoring will continue until issuance of your SI and then, with some modifications, for the duration of your SI which, depending on the decision of the FAA (and the recommendation of your IMS), might be anywhere from five years (rarely the claimed minimum of three years) up to the duration of your career.

References:

1. "Alcohol, anti-depressants, and the FAA," *Flying Magazine*, November 4, 2011, https://www.flyingmag.com/pilots-places/pilots-adventures-more/alcohol-antidepressants-and-faa
2. FAA DUI information is available at: https://www.faa.gov/about/office_org/headquarters_offices/ash/ash_programs/investigations/airmen_duidwi/
3. FAA, "Alcohol and Flying," www.faa.gov/pilots/safety/pilotsafetybrochures/media/alcohol.pdf
4. HIMS AMEs: https://www.faa.gov/pilots/amelocator/media/HIMS%20INDEPENDENT%20MEDICAL%20SPONSORS.pdf
5. "FAA CERTIFICATION AID: Drug and Alcohol Monitoring Recertification," (updated 11/30/2016): https://www.faa.gov/about/office_org/headquarters_offices/avs/offices/aam/ame/guide/media/Drug_Alcohol_Monitoring_Recertification_Aid.pdf
6. "AOPA Substance Abuse: Specifications for Psychiatric and Psychological Evaluation," www.aopa.org/go-fly/medical-resources/health-conditions/substance-abuse/specifications-for-psychiatric-and-psychological-evaluation
7. "Guide for Aviation Medical Examiners, Decision Considerations, Disease Protocols, Psychiatric and Psychological Evaluations": https://www.faa.gov/about/office_org/headquarters_offices/avs/offices/aam/ame/guide/dec_cons/disease_prot/ppevals/
8. CAGE questionnaire: https://www.mdcalc.com/cage-questions-alcohol-use
9. Alcohol Use Inventory (AUDIT): https://www.uky.edu/hr/sites/www.uky.edu.hr/files/worklife/documents/worklife_alcoholUseInventory.pdf
10. Substance Abuse Subtle Screening Inventory (SASSI): https://pubs.niaaa.nih.gov/publications/assessingalcohol/InstrumentPDFs/66_SASSI.pdf
11. Diagnostic Interview Schedule-IV (DIS-IV): https://pubs.niaaa.nih.gov/publications/assessingalcohol/instrumentpdfs/23_dis-iv.pdf

12. Addiction Severity Index (ASI): http://www.bu.edu/igsw/online-courses/substanceabuse/AddictionSeverityIndex,5thedition.pdf

13. "HIMS Recommended Practices": Treatment: http://www.himsprogram.com/Content/RP_Treatment

14. As an example, check: https://casapalmera.com/treatments/professional-pilots-treatment-program/

15. "Cog Screen": Check the following three sites:
    https://www.cogscreen.com/
    http://www.cogscreen.com/Overview.aspx
    http://www.cogscreen.com/2016Seminar/Kay-CogScreenFundamentalsAPS2016.pdf

16. "HIMS Aftercare/Monitoring": www.himsprogram.com/Content/Aftercare

17. Soberlink®: https://www.soberlink.com/

Chapter 7
Navigating HIMS: Your 'SI' and Beyond

Disclaimer: I have extensively researched HIMS requirements via FAA materials, HIMS program materials, airline HIMS manuals and, where possible, interviews with HIMS personnel. Unfortunately, neither the FAA nor airlines are particularly transparent about how the general guidelines they list are actually applied, presumably to better consolidate control over people who don't understand what is being done to them. Nor are HIMS program requirements consistent between different programs or participants. Accordingly, variation from what you read below is possible. If you experience something at variance with what I outline, please report what you experience at HIMSNightmare.com.

Time to apply for a medical certificate?

So let's say you've played "dancing bear" for the last six (or many more) months, complying with HIMS' various demands and convincing everyone you are sufficiently recovered. With the permission of your overseers, you think it is time to apply for your Special Issuance Medical Certificate (SI).

Not so fast, bucko: you have additional hurdles to clear, the first of which is the "Psychiatric and Psychological Evaluation" (P&P). In order to facilitate recovery of cognitive abilities potentially impaired by chronic substance abuse, the FAA requires at least 30 days after release from residential treatment before the P&P, ensuring the pilot has at least 60 days of sobriety. However, chronic heavy use of alcohol may require longer cognitive recovery periods. After suboptimal performance on a P&P, the FAA will generally require six months before retesting,[1] so don't rush things.

Psychiatric and Psychological (P&P) Evaluations

For a summary of the test battery administered during cognitive testing, check "Neurocognitive Assessment of Pilots: The FAA Perspective."[2] Although the battery of tests utilized for cognitive evaluation is not fixed, the FAA encourages the use of CogScreen-AE because "CogScreen is a valid predictor of both flight training and flight performance."[3] As preparation for cognitive testing, many pilots find it helpful to work exercises from Lumosity[4] and Brain HQ[5] regimens.

Neurocognitive evaluation

The core test battery must include:[6]

- ❏ CogScreen-Aeromedical Edition (CogScreen-AE)
- ❏ The complete Wechsler Adult Intelligence Scales
- ❏ Trail Making Test, Parts A and B (Reitan Trails A & B)
- ❏ Executive function tests to include:
  1) Category Test or Wisconsin Card Sorting Test, and
  2) Stroop Color-Word Test
- ❏ Paced Auditory Serial Addition Test (PASAT)
- ❏ A continuous performance test (i.e., Test of Variables of Attention [TOVA], or Conners' Continuous Performance Test [CPT-II], or Integrated Visual and Auditory Continuous Performance Test [IVA+]), or Gordon Diagnostic System [GDS].
- ❏ Test of verbal memory (WMS-IV subtests, Rey Auditory Verbal Learning Test, or California Verbal Learning Test-II)
- ❏ Test of visual memory (WMS-IV subtests, Brief Visuospatial Memory Test-Revised, or Rey Complex Figure Test)
- ❏ Tests of Language including Boston Naming Test and Verbal Fluency (COWAT and a semantic fluency task)
- ❏ Psychomotor testing including Finger Tapping and Grooved Pegboard or Purdue Pegboard
- ❏ Personality testing, to include the Minnesota Multiphasic Personality Inventory (MMPI-2). (The MMPI-2-RF is not an approved substitute.)

Psychiatric evaluation

According to FAA, the evaluation must include at a minimum:[7]

- ❏ A review of all available records, including academic records, records of prior psychiatric hospitalizations, and records of periods of observation or treatment (e.g., psychiatrist, psychologist, social worker, counselor, or neuropsychologist treatment notes). Records must be in sufficient detail to permit a clear evaluation of the nature and extent of any previous mental disorders.
- ❏ A thorough clinical interview to include a detailed history regarding: psychosocial or developmental problems; academic and employment performance; legal issues; substance use/abuse (including treatment and quality of recovery); aviation background and experience; medical conditions together with all medication used; and behavioral observations during the interview.
- ❏ A mental status examination.
- ❏ An integrated summary of findings with an explicit diagnostic statement, and the psychiatrist's opinion(s) and recommendation(s) for treatment, medication, therapy, counseling, rehabilitation, or monitoring should be explicitly stated. Opinions regarding clinically or aeromedically significant findings and the potential impact on aviation safety must be consistent with the Federal Aviation Regulations.

Neuropsychological evaluation

According to FAA, the evaluation must include at a minimum:[8]

- ❏ A review of all available records, including academic records, records of prior psychiatric hospitalizations, and records of periods of observation or treatment (e.g., psychiatrist, psychologist, social worker, counselor, or neuropsychologist treatment notes).
- ❏ A thorough clinical interview to include a detailed history regarding: psychosocial or developmental problems; academic and employment performance; legal issues; substance use/abuse (in-

cluding treatment and quality of recovery); aviation background and experience; medical conditions, and all medication used; and behavioral observations during the interview.
- ❑ A mental status examination.
- ❑ An integrated summary of findings with an explicit diagnostic statement, the psychiatrist's opinion(s) and recommendation(s) for treatment, medication, therapy, counseling, rehabilitation, or monitoring should be explicitly stated.

So you 'passed' the P&P...

Getting your SI

With the blessing of your IMS, you may now take your FAA medical exam. (See Appendix D.) Your IMS will compile all of the FAA-mandated information, including the recommendation from the psychiatrist, and submit it to the FAA. Then you wait ... patiently. (We are told that pestering the FAA might actually delay issuance of your SI. Once again, you are at the mercy of your overseers.) Sixty to ninety days (or more) for processing of your package is not uncommon.

While waiting for your SI, you will continue the monitoring and other requirements (HIMS meetings, peer monitor contacts, aftercare, substance monitoring) as dictated by the shrink. In fact, whatever he prescribes will likely be required for the five years (or more) you are required to maintain a SI. Again, although you may be told by (perhaps deliberately) optimistic HIMS representatives that SIs may be required for as few as three years, in truth you will probably be committed for five years or more, up to and potentially including the remainder of your career.

Seven likely conditions of your Special Issuance Authorization (SIA)

- ❑ Continuing recovery including complete abstinence from mood-altering substances for as long as you hold an FAA medical certificate

- ❏ AA participation as stipulated in the SIA (typically at least three AA meetings per week)
- ❏ Monthly reports from flight operations supervisor
- ❏ Monthly reports from union representative (peer monitor)
- ❏ Quarterly reports from group aftercare provider
- ❏ Annual reports from psychiatrist
- ❏ Additional stipulated requirements

Note: *Additional requirements, up to and including regaining FAA airman certificates, may pertain if you received a DOT violation or violation of company policy. For an example of SIA conditions, see Appendix E.*

Your personal statement to the FAA

Oh, one more thing: If the self-flagellation you enjoyed in rehab and beyond has not been enough to satisfy the masochistic lust necessary to succeed in HIMS, you must now write a letter to the FAA confessing to your sins prior to recovery and telling them how grateful you are to everyone who has flogged you. Without this, no SI for you.

Oops, you 'slipped'[9]

So, Mr. or Mrs. Recovery, we had a little drinkie, did we? What happens next is widely variable depending on a number of things, not the least of which is how supplicant you are. You might get a little slap that results in nothing more than re-education, or you might get sent back to rehab for 28 days and have to do the whole thing all over. If you relapse prior to the SI, the FAA considers it a slightly less serious "slip." If you relapse after the SI, it is a "relapse," per the FAA, with greater ramifications.

Generally, the consequences are less serious if you self-report than if you get caught, although I have heard of one gent who tested positive and got a chance to "self-report," as in: "So, Ed. Is there anything you would like to tell us?"

The consensus seems to be that HIMS participants tend to relapse not only in response to stress, but even positive change. They call these "risk points." One guy I met at rehab was just about to get his SI when he discovered that forgotten bottle of vodka while cleaning out his car.

You will hear endlessly about your "triggers" – events, places or things that might induce you to relapse. You will also hear constantly that relapse is a process, not a single event, and is supposedly preceded by a mode of thinking which induces the relapse. If you relapse, your overseers will regard you as either refusing to believe you have "the disease" or not believing the disease is as powerful and unpredictable as they constantly tell you it is. They will actively look for examples of this "relapse thinking" and, if you exhibit them, it's back to re-education for you.

Note: The FAA considers use of non-alcoholic beer or wine, or the sleeping aid Ambien to be a relapse.

Top 7 relapse precursors NOT to let your overseers see

- Failure to comply with HIMS program requirements
- Failure to comply with rules of recovery as they are dictated to you
- Decisions which might lead to the dreaded "hungry, angry, lonely, or tired" (HALT)
- Being cavalier about being around alcohol (e.g. hanging out at bars with friends)
- Demonstrating anger, resentment, or criticism (which your overseers might deliberately induce to get rid of you)
- Lack of acceptance of occurrences deemed by your overseers to be "beyond your control" (which includes anything they decide)
- Excessive optimism. (No, I'm not kidding. Although you are expected to be in a "pink cloud" early in recovery due to the supposed wonders you are experiencing, if you are excessively rosy later on, you will get the squinty-eyed glare of appraisal because they will regard you as potentially "self-delusional.")

Personally, I had virtually no desire to consume alcohol during my sentence in HIMS, perhaps because I wasn't nearly as "alcoholic" as the Spanish Inquisition tortured me into confessing, but also because I wouldn't give the pricks the satisfaction of seeing me fail. (Oops. It seems I still have to work on those "resentments.") And (admittedly on no hard evidence) I truly believe there are a few HIMS bureaucrats – principally those in recovery themselves – who *want* to see you fail. Beyond job security, the fact that they've stayed "sober" while you didn't gives them a sense of superiority, especially if they had relapsed themselves a time or two ... or ten. For example, I can't tell you the number of times the shrink – during sessions that were supposed to be for evaluating *me* – endlessly pontificated on his thirty years of sobriety, while threatening me with a diagnosis of "narcissistic personality disorder."

Five consequences to expect if your overseers suspect impending relapse (in order)

- You will be grounded
- All HIMS team members will be notified
- The inquisition will begin
- You will be remanded to re-education (Oops, sorry. I meant "the appropriate treatment option.")
- A letter may be sent to the FAA, potentially resulting in the withdrawal of your SI

Relapse re-education

This is euphemistically referred to as "re-treatment" and will vary with your willingness to disclose and the type and severity of substance use. Although the FAA permits unlimited tries, expect your company to shift more of the financial burden onto you. If you lapse with a single episode, don't expect to be believed that it was only once, and the HIMS program strongly urges substance abuse professionals to consider you a liar if you say so. If you relapse once, you will be expected to do it again. Additionally, if you previously received five years or less of monitoring, after a relapse you can expect monitoring for the duration of your career.

Operating under your SI

You will receive a "Special Issuance Authorization" (SIA) with your medical certificate which stipulates the conditions under which you may exercise the privileges of your medical. Although your Independent Medical Sponsor (IMS) will assist in making sure you are in compliance, such compliance is ultimately your responsibility.

Typical continuing requirements

- Monthly monitor meetings with your chief pilot, HIMS personnel and your IMS (who must certify you every six months)
- Periodic check-in with your peer monitor (typically four times per month)
- Group aftercare (typically two times per month after issuance of the SI)
- Drug and alcohol testing (typically 14 times per year, although I have heard of programs using Soberlink® for the entire duration of participation)
- Annual meeting with your HIMS-designated psychiatrist

Each time you take a medical exam, your Aviation Medical Examiner (AME) will need a letter from your IMS beforehand.

Medical procedures

Each and every time you have a medical procedure that requires any potentially addictive pain medication, you must provide all relevant information to your IMS beforehand, up to and potentially including photos of the labels for medications prescribed. When my drug test came back positive for oxazepam, the only thing that saved me was being able to document a surgical procedure that required Valium (diazepam) and a letter from my doctor noting that oxazepam was a metabolite of Valium. All of this went into my permanent medical record.

Four ways out of HIMS

1. Your IMS agrees to petition for release from monitoring (unlikely until the end of your SI)
2. You get ejected from the program or terminated
3. You withdraw from the program and find your own IMS. On this one, expect considerable pushback from the company, as outlined in Chapter 2 under "Company abuses"
4. You retire … or commit suicide (just kidding … sort of)

What happens when you say 'I want *my* cigarettes…'

In *One Flew Over the Cuckoo's Nest*, the ordinarily submissive Mr. Cheswick, inspired by agitator Randle Patrick McMurphy, repeatedly disrupts a group therapy session to demand his cigarettes be returned to him by the ever-domineering Nurse Rached. In the ensuing melee, orderlies begin dragging away patients.

With only slightly greater subtlety, that's pretty much what you can expect if you have the gall to demand fairness and rationality from HIMS. Your compliant will draw a patronizingly sympathetic response, of course. But you will not see that, on the other end of the phone line, the hand connected to that soothing voice is writing case notes branding you as a troublemaker.

All is not what it seems. Unknown to you, HIMS bureaucrats busily justify their existence by writing reams of case notes and emails describing your every comment and behavior in terms that are generally unflattering, often inaccurate, and sometimes downright fictitious. I know this because I demanded my medical files, which my overseers relinquished only upon threat of HIPAA action by a lawyer. What I got stretched to 1600 pages.

Any attempt on your part to influence the outcome of your case will draw withering fire. "Control," you see, is something you must not have. Only "powerlessness" will suffice. As for the practical application of this enforced "powerlessness," addiction journalist Maia Szalavitz writes: "A treatment philosophy that contends that it is acceptable to treat 'powerless' people as such—and to rub their faces in it with strict rules and restrictions—creates a program that inevitably abuses those who are in its care."[10]

If you want to stay under the radar, remain calm at all times – regardless of what humiliation you are dealt. The tactic typically used to cull you from the herd is to inflict upon you something which would outrage any sane person and then, when you react, say, "See? I thought so. He's very impulsive. We should send him to anger management counseling."

Another favorite is to use a variation of a semi-slanderous political tactic I call "some say" (as in *Some say* you club baby seals for sport"). Here they will claim that unnamed co-workers such as flight attendants or customer service personnel report you as confrontational, difficult to work with, etc. What they never seem to recount are the specifics of those reports. When I challenged one HIMS bureaucrat over unsubstantiated allegations made to my psychiatrist, she denied ever having made them.

The single riskiest word you can use is, "Why?" Asking questions such as, "Why am I being urine tested for the third time this week?" or "Why am I being required to do four AA meetings per week when other people only get three?" will bring you to the attention of people whose attention you **Do. Not. Want.**

Although there are, unsurprisingly, no statistics tracking reasons for failure in HIMS, conversations with some of its many victims suggest most are ejected for reasons not directly related to substance abuse. Instead, they are saddled with a second disqualifying diagnosis, typically some manner of "personality disorder," and either fired or left to languish in medical purgatory.

References:

1. "Recommended Practices: Medical Re-certification": http://www.himsprogram.com/Content/RP_ReCert
2. "Neurocognitive Assessment of Pilots: The FAA Perspective": http://civilavmed.org/wp-content/uploads/2016/03/Neurocognitive-Assessment-The-FAA-Perspective_CAMA-Sunday-at-AsMA-2017.pdf
3. "Cog Screen": https://www.cogscreen.com/
4. Lumosity: https://www.lumosity.com/
5. Brain HQ: https://www.brainhq.com/
6. "Specifications for Psychiatric and Neuropsychological Evaluations for Substance Abuse/Dependence": https://www.faa.gov/about/office_org/headquarters_offices/avs/offices/aam/ame/guide/media/substanceabuseevalspecs.pdf
7. Ibid.
8. Ibid.
9. HIMS "Recommended Practices: Relapse Issues": http://www.himsprogram.com/Content/RP_Relapse
10. Maia Szalavitz, "What I've Finally Concluded About 12-Step Programs After 25 Years Writing About Drugs and Addiction," Pacific Standard, June 14, 2017, https://psmag.com/social-justice/ive-finally-concluded-12-step-programs-25-years-writing-drugs-addiction-91099

Chapter 8
Substance Testing & Monitoring

Writing this chapter scared even me. The question is not whether you will get caught for something you did, which is inevitable; it is whether you will get caught for something you *didn't* do. If you are thinking, "I don't take any drugs, so I don't have anything to worry about," see previous descriptions of my experience with false positives. In particular, one airline is reportedly experiencing false positives on blood testing for alcohol metabolites.

Types of drug and alcohol testing

1. Pre-Employment (drugs only)
2. Reasonable Suspicion
3. Post-Accident
4. Return-To-Duty
5. Random Selection ("DOT testing")

In HIMS, the substance abuse testing you will most commonly encounter will largely fall under the sub-categories of initial evaluation and monitoring for abstinence, both of which are loosely connected to category number four above. For initial testing and evaluation, you can count on a blood test, including PEth, described below, which can detect chronic alcohol use for a month or more. Abstinence monitoring is generally done via urine testing, although your HIMS program might also do occasional blood tests.

Drug and alcohol testing in general

Drug and alcohol tests do not just look for the drug in your blood, urine or saliva. They look for "biomarkers" of the substance used, which can also be stored in hair, fatty cells, and nails. The greater your percentage of body fat, the longer the biomarkers can be identified. Indeed, depending on the test, they can be identified for a month or more. If you use a substance chronically, the window during which you may test positive may be significantly longer than for an occasional user. And if your rate of metabolism is slow (e.g. if you are in suboptimal health), detection windows increase.

This section is more heavily oriented toward alcohol testing, since random DOT testing for pilots makes it unlikely that a chronic user of illegal drugs would progress very far into a flying career (notwithstanding the idiotic movie *Flight* depicting Denzel Washington snorting cocaine prior to reporting for duty).

Variables impacting metabolism of alcohol and drugs

- General health
- Age
- Metabolic rate
- Body mass/body fat
- Level of chronic use
- Level of physical activity

Urine testing

The "gold standard" for alcohol testing in urine is EtG (ethyl glucuronide), which is extremely sensitive and can detect even low levels of alcohol. The claimed maximum for detecting alcohol in urine is five days, but chronic users should consider the possibility that it might be longer. Recent scientific studies have identified ethyl sulfate (EtS) as a second specific metabolite or biomarker of ethanol, so alcohol testing may include both.

Note that even a single drink can be detected for a number of hours after consumption. A common "WAG" is that a single episode of high alcohol consumption (not chronic drinking) can be detected up to 80 hours after consumption. In one study, 17 test subjects were administered high levels of alcohol. EtG levels were tested eight times over a

102 hour period after drinking. In the first 24 hours after drinking, all EtG tests were positive. After 54 hours, 77% of results were positive. Even after 78.5 hours, 18% were positive.[1]

It is important to note that although EtG will be used to monitor your compliance once in HIMS, it is *not* the preferred method for initial evaluation of substance abuse/dependence. That will be the much more far-ranging PEth (phosphatidylethanol) blood test described below.

In terms of drug testing, the HIMS website referenced previously notes that urine screens used for DOT testing utilize a "five-panel" test. DOT drug testing typically uses immunoassay for the initial screening and gas chromatography/mass spectrometry (GC/MS) for confirmation. The so-called "NIDA 5" (for "National Institute of Drug Abuse")[2] include:

- Opiates
- Cocaine
- Marijuana
- Phencyclidine (PCP)
- Amphetamines/methamphetamines

Abstinence compliance testing typically uses a 10 or 12-panel test, including:

- Cocaine
- Marijuana
- Phencyclidine (PCP)
- Amphetamines
- Opiates
- Benzodiazepines
- Barbiturates
- Methadone
- Propoxyphene
- Quaaludes
- Ecstasy/MDA
- Oxycodone/Percoset

Other tests may involve hair and nail samples, with the detection window varying with drug consumed, amount consumed, and method of testing employed.

Blood testing

Your initial substance abuse evaluation will include a blood test, including a PEth (phosphatidylethanol) test, which measures direct biomarkers and is considered an accurate indicator of steady moderate and "binge" consumption, but is less sensitive to low levels of consumption.

Although PEth is used to detect chronic alcohol consumption, in truth a single "binge drinking" episode could produce high PEth levels and a subsequent diagnosis of "Alcohol Use Disorder" per DSM-5 (the *Diagnostic and Statistical Manual of Mental Disorders*).[3]

A positive PEth result is a reading of 20 ng/mL or above, which is interpreted to represent "excessive alcohol abuse." A result of over 100 ng/mL is considered to be strong evidence of heavy binge drinking. It is typically claimed that PEth is detectable for two to three weeks but, in truth, it may be detectable for far longer depending on how much alcohol was consumed and for how long. Some anecdotes suggest detection up to *six weeks*.

Abstinence monitoring

Beef Bourguignon and 'the slippery slope'

In HIMS, you will be told repeatedly about all the things you cannot ingest, not only because they might cause you to test positive on your random monitoring, but also because they might be "The Beginning of the End." At a HIMS meeting, an addiction physician once advised us that eating Beef Bourguignon would start us down the slippery slope toward relapse. Seriously.

Over-the-counter meds

Mouthwash containing alcohol is definitely out of the question (non-alcoholic types are available), as is any over-the-counter medication containing alcohol (e.g. NyQuil™). Unfortunately, the list of prohibited meds is long. You could potentially get into trouble using any medication containing the abbreviation "DM" or "DXM" (dextromethorphan), such as Mucinex® DM, Robitussin® DM and others. DXM can test positive for PCP (phencyclidine) and reportedly stays in the bloodstream for 11-22 hours, or even up to 33 hours for those with slow metabolism. Similarly, Sudaphed® (pseudoephedrine) can cause a false positive for amphetamine and Sudaphed® PE can test positive for methamphetamine.

The good news is that the false positives are generally on initial screening tests done by immunoassay. DOT testing (and presumably your abstinence monitoring) is verified using gas chromatography/mass spectometry (GC/MS), which should be able to distinguish between true and false positive results.

The bad news is that the facility to which you will be remanded for group aftercare will likely do their own testing (reportedly for insurance purposes), which might *not* use the relatively expensive GC/MS. At my company, I was assured that any initial positive from an aftercare facility would be confirmed using GC/MS. Check with your HIMS personnel for specifics.

Non-alcoholic beer and wine

As previously stated, the FAA considers drinking non-alcoholic beer and wine to be a "relapse." Their logic is likely threefold: First, many "alcohol-free" wines and beers are not actually alcohol-free, but instead may have up to about 0.5% alcohol. Second, substance abuse professionals fear the "slippery slope," wherein you start feeling in control of your life again (heaven forbid) and begin to revert to the nasty old habits they spent so much time and effort to re-educate out of you. Third, non-alcoholic beer and wine is considered to be a "trigger" which may lead to relapse. Although I can find nothing specifically addressing the topic, for those reasons I suspect the FAA would take a dim view of even those which have 0% alcohol content, despite the fact that the Code of Federal Regulations defines "alcoholic beverage" as "any beverage in liquid form which contains not less than one-half of one percent (.5%) of alcohol by volume".

Cooking with alcohol

Although conventional wisdom maintains that alcohol evaporates during cooking, in truth it depends on the duration and method used. Full removal of alcohol can take up to three hours of cooking. When adding wine to sauce in a sauté pan, references say to allow for 20-30 seconds of cooking to remove alcohol. However, a pot roast simmered in wine may take 2 ½ hours of cooking or more.[4] Of course, one might conjecture that low levels of alcohol remaining after such cooking might not be detectable with EtG testing, but that call is up to you. (Slugging out of the bottle while cooking is definitely a no-no.)

Just a few from among the long list of foods you will no longer be approved to eat are: Penne alla Vodka (obviously), Veal Marsala (marsala), wine vinegar (wine), Dijon mustard (wine), sauces such as béarnaise or bordelaise (wine), fondue (wine), liqueur-filled chocolates, vanilla (unspecified alcohol), honeybuns (God knows what), and even an authentic presentation of French onion soup (cognac).

In summary, if you mention to your overseers either cooking with alcohol or eating foods containing alcohol, you can expect problems.

Prescription drugs

Top 3 rules of prescription medication for HIMS:

1. Declare to your HIMS overseers any prescription medication even remotely likely to test positive on a drug screen. (That was what

saved me from near doom following a false positive on a benzodiazepine called Serax, a drug I had never even heard of much less taken. For details, see Chapter 4.)
2. Don't take drugs prescribed for others.
3. Don't take drugs which were prescribed for you but for a different time or illness – a practice which, like number two above, could also give you a DOT positive drug test, whether or not you are in HIMS.

Fooling the drug test

The Internet is alive with theories and devices designed to "fool" drug testing regimens. I'm not going to cover these, since most of them are crap and, even if they do ameliorate drug screen results, might cause the sample to come back as adulterated. So, on this one, I regret to say you are on your own.

Other substances

When you start abstinence monitoring, you will receive a ridiculously long list of *non*-ingestible substances (e.g. cleaning fluids, colognes, bug sprays, hand sanitizers) which can also trigger a positive test for alcohol (after which you will probably develop a pathological aversion to ever touching anything again without rubber gloves, or to breathing without a surgical mask). Such are the many gifts of HIMS.

False positives

False positives on urine tests are a distinct possibility, particularly with immunoassay testing. They are less likely with GC/MS. The generally accepted claim is that PEth produces no false positives, although one can both find anecdotes and research that hand sanitizer – particularly when fumes are inhaled – can affect PEth results.

> **The 'infallible' PEth test ... and you**
>
> Despite assertions that false positives are impossible with PEth tests, I have spoken with at least two individuals who experienced them. In one case, the captain was met by company representatives at an outstation and escorted outside security, where his company ID was confiscated. He contracted his own independent test, which came back negative, and he was reinstated. At another company, however, the pilot got his own independent blood and hair tests, which came back negative, only to have the company refuse to accept them. His company demanded another 90-day (yes, 90-day!) rehab for his "relapse." When he refused, the company terminated him. Although I have been unable to confirm it, apocryphal evidence suggests that using dried blood spot testing and failing to allow blood samples to adequately dry may effectively permit fermentation of blood sugar, producing false positive results. By contrast, other drug testing laboratories which do whole blood testing might avoid the problem.

References:

1. "Sensitivity of commercial ethyl glucuronide (ETG) testing in screening for alcohol abstinence," *Alcohol and Alcoholism*, Volume 42, Issue 4, 1 July 2007, pp. 317–320, https://doi.org/10.1093/alcalc/agm014
2. "FAA Medical Certification & Drug Testing," Pilot Medical Solutions, Inc., https://www.leftseat.com/faa-medical-certification-drug-testing/
3. *Diagnostic and Statistical Manual of Mental Disorders* (5th ed.; DSM–5; American Psychiatric Association, 2013).
4. "Alcohol Evaporation in Cooking and Baking," What's Cooking America, https://whatscookingamerica.net/Q-A/AlcoholEvap.htm

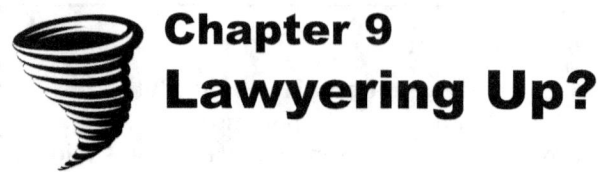
Chapter 9
Lawyering Up?

Disclaimer: I am not a lawyer and nothing herein constitutes legal advice!

So, you think you aren't getting a fair shake from the HIMS program? Maybe the company is abusing the program to target you? It is easy enough to say "I'm gonna sue!" The reality, however, is much more (if you'll permit me the pun) sobering.

The good news is that you might be covered under the Americans with Disabilities Act. The bad news is that there are multiple steps required before filing a discrimination lawsuit. To sue, you must first file a complaint with the Equal Employment Opportunity Commission (EEOC). Only after you have obtained a "right to sue" letter from them can you file a lawsuit against your employer.

Pursuing the steps necessary for legal action against your company will require time, dedication, organization, and money, perhaps exceeding even that required to pursue independent medical recertification. Even with a strong case, resolution might take years and tens of thousands of dollars.

You will be all alone. Company and HIMS personnel will treat you like a pariah. Peers may dismiss you as a malcontent. Potential lawyers may see you as marginal and unprofitable. Your AA sponsor will say you are harboring "justified resentment." (Are you?) Idiots will predict your failure, insisting "You can't fight city hall." Even family and friends will shake their heads and say: "Are you really sure you want to do this?"

Be ready to be called crazy. As previously mentioned, a popular way to get rid of malcontents in HIMS is to diagnose them with "personality disorders," rendering them potentially ineligible for FAA medical certificates. Worse, the very act of defending yourself against accusations of mental illness could be depicted as a symptom of mental illness.

To quote a mock-Latin phrase from *The Handmaid's Tale*, "Nolite te bastardes carborundorum," which (if it were real Latin) would translate to "Don't let the bastards grind you down." Your torturers might even try to get you to act out of frustration in order to depict you as volatile, even dangerous. If you let them get to you, you lose.

Ask yourself, "How bad do I want it?" If you are truly "in denial" about alcoholism or out for simple revenge, you may lack the objectivity necessary to succeed. Personally, I find it difficult (read that "impossible") to simply walk away when I have been wronged. In such cases, I am willing to go to great lengths to secure justice. But that's just me. You must objectively and critically evaluate whether you have the fortitude to navigate this uniquely tortuous journey.

The following steps are necessary to pursue action against your company. More than likely, they can't be shortcutted. As previously noted, an EEOC compliant must precede litigation. A complaint to your human relations department (or "People Department" or "Team Member Experience Department" or whatever other Orwellian name your company uses to disguise its means of getting rid of you) must precede the EEOC complaint.

Without documentation, you will lose. If you have ignored my previous advice to keep copious records of everything done to you and by you, start doing it now. Keep emails, letters, drug and alcohol testing records, telephone logs, pay stubs, and records of meetings. If you are operating in a "one-party consent" state – where recordings of phone calls and meetings require the consent of only one of the parties being recorded (namely, you), consider recording such contacts. (Note: The fact that it is legal doesn't mean it is permissible by company policy.) If you are lied to—which is by no means novel in HIMS—you will need documentation to prove it.

Discrimination claims

Alcoholism

As a recovering alcoholic or illegal drug user, you will likely be covered by the Americans with Disabilities Act (ADA), but "recovering" is the key word; nothing under the ADA protects you if you are an active alcoholic or currently using illegal drugs, particularly on the job.

The ADA National Network[1] states:

> *"Are alcoholics protected by the ADA?*
>
> *"They may be. While a current illegal user of drugs is not protected by the ADA if an employer acts on the basis of such use, a person who currently uses alcohol is not automatically denied protection. Alcoholism is an impairment, and if it substantially limits a major life activity (e.g., learning, concentrating, interacting with others, caring for oneself) it will constitute a disability. An alcoholic may be a person with a disability and protected by the ADA if s/he is qualified to perform the essential functions of the job. An employer may be required to provide an accommodation to an alcoholic (e.g. a flexible schedule to enable the employee to attend counseling appointments).*
>
> *"However, an employer can discipline, discharge or deny employment to an alcoholic whose use of alcohol adversely affects job performance or conduct. An employer also may prohibit the use of alcohol in the workplace and can require that employees not be under the influence of alcohol."*

Given that you must be "qualified to perform the essential functions of the job," one might argue that you can only avail yourself of the ADA once you receive your Special Issuance Medical Certificate (SI), but I leave that question to better legal minds than mine.

Illegal drug use

Similarly, the ADA protects those "who have been successfully rehabilitated and who are no longer engaged in the illegal use of drugs; who are currently participating in a rehabilitation program and are no longer engaging in the illegal use of drugs; [or] who are regarded, erroneously, as illegally using drugs." [2]

Following is a summary of rights and responsibilities from the U.S. Civil Rights Commission:[3]

- An individual who is currently engaging in the illegal use of drugs is not an "individual with a disability" when the employer acts on the basis of such use.
- An employer may not discriminate against a person who has a history of drug addiction but who is not currently using drugs and who has been rehabilitated.
- An employer may prohibit the illegal use of drugs and the use of alcohol at the workplace.
- It is not a violation of the ADA for an employer to give tests for the illegal use of drugs.
- An employer may discharge or deny employment to persons who currently engage in the illegal use of drugs.
- Employees who use drugs or alcohol may be required to meet the same standards of performance and conduct that are set for other employees.

What constitutes discrimination?

During pre-employment screening, an employer may ask whether an applicant drinks alcohol or whether he or she is currently using drugs illegally. They may *not*, however, ask whether an applicant is a drug abuser or alcoholic, or inquire whether he or she has ever been in a drug or alcohol rehabilitation program.

In the workplace, employers must provide "reasonable accommodation" for treatment of alcoholism, such as leave to seek medical treatment. Accordingly, one might argue that one could not be terminated or disciplined specifically because he or she is *successfully* participating in an alcohol treatment program. (Unsuccessful participation would be a different matter.) Similarly, some have argued, with varying success depending on the strength of the claim, that they were subjected to discrimination and harassment due to their status as recovering alcoholics.

Retaliation claims

Although they might try, your employer cannot legally punish you for filing a complaint of discrimination under the ADA. According to the EEOC:

> *"The federal employment discrimination laws depend on the willingness of employees and applicants to challenge discrimination without fear of punishment. Individuals rely on the statutory prohibitions against retaliation, also known as 'reprisal,' when they complain to an employer about an alleged equal employment opportunity (EEO) violation, provide information as a witness in a company or agency investigation, or file a charge with the Equal Employment Opportunity Commission..."*[4]

What constitutes 'opposition'?

An individual is protected from retaliation for opposing any practice made unlawful under the Equal Employment Opportunity (EEO) laws. Protected "opposition" encompasses methods by which an individual may communicate, explicitly or implicitly, in opposition to perceived employment discrimination. Opposition must be "reasonable," and must be based on good faith belief that the conduct opposed is unlawful.

The "opposition clause" of Title VII protects workers who oppose discriminatory actions by their employers, including:

- Reporting a violation to your employer;
- Complaints to someone other than employer;
- Complaints raised publicly; or
- Advising employer of intent to file, or complaining before matter is actionable.

When has 'retaliation' occurred?

According to the EEOC:

> "Retaliation occurs when an employer takes a materially adverse action because an individual has engaged in, or may engage in, activity in furtherance of the EEO laws the Commission enforces. The EEO anti-retaliation provisions ensure that individuals are free to raise complaints of potential EEO violations or engage in other EEO activity without employers taking materially adverse actions in response."[5]

What if the claim which precipitated retaliation is wrong?

Just because the actions on which the original discrimination claim was based turn out to be lawful, the claim of retaliation will not be rendered invalid, provided the original complaint was made in good faith.

According to the EEOC:

> "As with participation, a retaliation claim based on opposition is not defeated merely because the underlying challenged practice ultimately is found to be lawful. For statements or actions to be protected opposition, however, they must be based on a reasonable good faith belief that the conduct opposed violates the EEO laws, or could do so if repeated. Because there is conduct that falls short of an actual violation but could be reasonably perceived to violate Title VII, the reasonable belief standard can apply to protect complainants as well as witnesses or bystanders who intervene or report what was observed."[6]

What are 'materially adverse actions'?

"Retaliation" occurs whenever an employer responds to a protected activity by taking a "materially adverse action," which is defined as any action which could deter a reasonable person from engaging in protected activity.

There are several categories of materially adverse actions:[7]

- **Work-related actions:** Examples include denial of promotion, refusal to hire, denial of job benefits, demotion, suspension, or discharge from a position. Other adverse actions may include threats, warnings, reprimands, transfers, negative or lowered evaluations, transfers to less desirable work or locations, or any other type of adverse treatment that might reasonably dissuade a person from engaging in protected activity.

- **Non-work-related actions:** A materially adverse action may also be an action that has no tangible effect on employment, or even an action that takes place outside of work, as long as it might reasonably dissuade a person from engaging in protected activity.

- **Other examples of materially adverse actions:**
    - Disparaging the person to others or in the media;
    - Making false reports to government authorities;
    - Filing a civil action;
    - Threatening reassignment;
    - Scrutinizing work performance more closely than that of other employees without justification;
    - Removal of supervisory responsibilities;
    - Abusive speech or acts reasonably likely to deter protected activity, even if not sufficiently severe or pervasive to create a hostile work environment;
    - Requiring re-verification of work status, making threats of deportation, or initiating action with immigration authorities due to protected activity;

- Terminating a union grievance process or otherwise blocking access to available remedial mechanisms;
- Taking or threatening a materially adverse action against a close family member (who could bring a claim in addition to the person who engaged in protected activity); or
- Any other action that might deter reasonable individuals from engaging in protected activity.

The five steps of pursuing action against your employer

What follows are the five steps for action in pursuing an ADA discrimination/retaliation complaint. Success lies in convincing your target that you are a serious person on serious business, and that you won't go away until achieving your objective.

Step #1:
Does collective bargaining apply?

The first question to answer is whether your particular issue is covered by a collective bargaining agreement (CBA). If so, the EEOC might not touch it and your only recourse might be filing a union grievance. For a better idea of whether an issue otherwise covered by collective bargaining is actionable through an EEOC complaint, I suggest legal consultation. It might cost you $300 or more, but will be money well spent.

That said, your HIMS program might not be covered by a union contract, even if you are subject to collective bargaining. Payroll issues, however, might be covered by the contract, meaning a grievance using your collective bargaining process might be the first step. That information may only be gleaned from a thorough reading of your contract and speaking with union representatives and lawyers.

Don't be discouraged if your CBA doesn't cover HIMS. As I began the process of pursuing action against my employer, I was at first disgusted by the fact that my union contract didn't protect me. When I later spoke to HIMS victims from other airlines, however, I began to regard it as a blessing rather than a curse. Even when a CBA applies, union representatives are generally loath to defend "drunks" whom they generally regard as the cause of their own misfortune.

Step #2:
Filing an HR complaint

Presuming research indicates your complaint is actionable, the first step is to make a complaint to your human relations (HR) department. I recommend at least consulting a lawyer, since you most definitely do *not* want to look like a lightweight who will be easily brushed aside.

Documentation is key. HR is not your friend; it is a protective mechanism for the corporation. Anything you can do to move the ball beyond "He said, she said…" will bolster your case.

Top 10 rules for making an HR complaint:

1. **Be objective:** Don't whine. Just because you don't like something doesn't make it actionable. Nobody wants to hear that your supervisor is being "mean" to you. Personal attacks or, worse, obscenities will fail. Your complaint must allege specific, objectively actionable offenses which involve materially adverse actions as described above.

2. **Do your research:** This book cites numerous resources from the EEOC and elsewhere. Start by looking them up and ensuring you have a legitimate case.

3. **Gather documentation:** You will need phone logs, emails, voicemails, letters, recordings of calls and meetings (if legal), and most of all a timeline of events.

4. **Be concise:** Nothing will make you look like a nutcase more than a 12-page rambling dissertation.

5. **Build a strong case:**
    - Carefully draft and edit your complaint as a document, not merely by filling out an online complaint form. If using such a form, copy and paste the document into the form once it has been completed elsewhere;
    - Write it objectively and dispassionately, not like a whine-fest from a petulant employee; and
    - Have someone else review the document for typos, errors, and general credibility.

6. **Follow HR procedures:** Review the employee handbook or online instructions to avoid giving the company an excuse for claiming that the complaint was not properly filed.

7. **Prepare to be questioned: This involves playing "what if." Corporate ethics being what they are, expect your company to distort events to blame everything on you. Questions to prepare for include, but are by no means limited to:**
    - What if they assert an alternative explanation of events?
    - What if they cite additional events you haven't considered?
    - What if they impugn your motives in making the complaint?

8. **Document how HR deals with your complaint:** If the corporation doesn't adequately resolve your problem, your next step is to file a complaint with EEOC. For that, you must be able to prove that HR failed to solve your issue and, if applicable, that they dealt with it unfairly.

9. **Don't necessarily discuss it with your chief pilot:** If your complaint is one of discrimination or retaliation under the ADA, your immediate supervisor might be the culprit. Don't give him an early heads up by notifying him of the complaint. Make it directly to your corporate HR or ethics investigation department.

10. **Define resolution:** What is it you are looking for? What is your *reasonable* desired outcome?

Large companies typically use an online portal to file complaints. I also recommend sending a certified letter to corporate officers who are directly responsible for such complaints, which will require research. Your goal is to stand out from the herd as a serious person on serious business, not a lightweight.

Step #3:
Filing an EEOC complaint

The EEOC enforces federal laws against discrimination due to an employee or job applicant's race, color, religion (or lack thereof), sex (including pregnancy, gender identity, and sexual orientation), national origin, age (40 or older), disability or genetic information. It is illegal for an employer to retaliate for complaining about discrimination, filing a charge of discrimination, or participating in an investigation or lawsuit. That said, be aware that the EEOC investigator assigned to your case is not your friend, but instead a necessary evil.

Compliant Timeline:

With some exceptions, anti-discrimination laws give you 180 calendar days from the day the discrimination took place to file a complaint with the EEOC. In some cases, the deadline may be extended to 300 days. Check the EEOC[8] website for information on your particular circumstance. (Note that federal employees and job applicants have a different complaint process and generally must contact an agency EEO Counselor within 45 days.)

According to the EEOC:

> "Time limits for filing a charge with EEOC generally will not be extended while you attempt to resolve a dispute through another forum such as an internal grievance procedure, a union grievance, arbitration or mediation before filing a charge with EEOC. Other forums for resolution may be pursued at the same time as the processing of the EEOC charge."[9]

Filing an EEOC discrimination complaint:

Repeat after me: "As a recovering alcoholic (or drug abuser) who has been abstinent and in perfect compliance with company requirements, I have been subjected by my employer to discrimination and (if appropriate) retaliation, resulting in materially adverse actions."

Those magic words will get you more action from the EEOC than the typically inarticulate "They done me wrong" that EEOC representatives are accustomed to hearing. Consider, too, that www.eeoc.gov will be your friend (or more likely not, since we are, after all, talking about a governmental website). Review eeoc.gov for all pertinent information, including discrimination, retaliation, adverse actions, and what you are entitled to do about them. In particular, see https://publicportal.eeoc.gov/Portal/Login.aspx.

Call the EEOC hotline (and be prepared to hold for most of an hour). Although some might consider this action redundant, the EEOC representative will give you a much better idea of what is involved in filing a complaint. When calling, the more prepared you are, the better the treatment you will receive. You will be told you need an intake interview, which can be scheduled by going through the rather lengthy registration process accessed via the "Public Portal" of the EEOC site. You will also be told that if no appointments are available within your 180-day time frame, check back daily for changes in the schedule. You can also do a walk-in to an EEOC office in your area without an appointment, but check hours and be prepared for a 2+-hour wait.

During the intake interview, you and an EEOC staff member will confidentially discuss your case, as well as your rights and responsibilities under the laws the EEOC enforces, the investigative process, and what to expect. The interview is not intended to resolve your complaint, only to ensure it is covered by the ADA.

The EEOC has 180 days to investigate your case, which may include witness interviews, requests for additional information, workplace visits, or attempts at mediation. While the EEOC might (rarely) sue, it generally issues either a "Letter of Determination" or a "Dismissal and Notice of Rights." Even if dismissed, you may then pursue litigation in the courts. If the Letter of Determination does not result in a settlement, or if the EEOC fails to resolve the issue within 180 days, you may request a "right to sue" letter, which you should retain for future litigation.

Step #4:
'Sue the Bastards!'

With either a "right to sue" letter or a "Dismissal and Notice of Rights" in hand, you have only **90 days** to file a lawsuit. If you have not already done so, immediately contact a lawyer experienced in employment law and begin negotiations and/or litigation.

Given that legal fees often start at around $300+ per hour and may total tens (or even hundreds) of thousands of dollars, finding a lawyer who will take your case on contingency is a serious plus. Typical contingency rates run about one-third of the recovery (40% if the case goes to trial), but a lawyer will take you on contingency only if you have a solid case likely to result in the award of significant damages. The good news is that some or all of the attorney fees may be recoverable under the ADA if the case goes to trial.

With luck (and a clear demonstration of organization and determination), you might be able to settle the case out of court. In either case, this is where your many months – or years – of scrupulous record-keeping and carefully planned actions will pay off.

References:

1. "Are alcoholics protected by the ADA?", ADA National Network: Information, Guidance and Training on the Americans with Disabilities Act, https://adata.org/faq/are-alcoholics-covered-ada
2. "Sharing the Dream: Is the ADA Accommodating All?", Chapter 4: Substance Abuse Under the ADA, https://www.usccr.gov/pubs/ada/ch4.htm

3. Ibid.
4. "EEOC Guidance on Retaliation and Related Issues," Equal Employment Opportunity Commission, https://www.eeoc.gov/laws/guidance/retaliation-guidance.cfm
5. Ibid.
6. Ibid.
7. Ibid.
8. Equal Opportunity Employment Commission: https://www.eeoc.gov/
9. EEOC "Time Limits for Filing a Charge", https://www.eeoc.gov/employees/timeliness.cfm

Chapter 10
To HIMS, or Not to HIMS?

As you have read many times in this book, I'm not telling you *not* to enter HIMS. I am merely saying that if the HIMS EF5 isn't bearing down on you, there are options less costly to your wallet, your lifestyle, and your personality. If you do choose to enter HIMS, I hope I've helped you better prepare for its pitfalls.

'You have a choice…'

The sages of AA and TSF (twelve-step facilitation therapy) are fond of telling you that "you always have a choice." What they fail to mention, of course, is that even the victims in the World Trade Center had a "choice" – to burn to death or jump 110 floors. Once you've been cornered in a burning building, nothing dictates that your "choices" are any good. If your medical is revoked or invalidated on grounds of substance abuse, your "choices" are to participate in HIMS or to end your career and with it, quite possibly, your lifestyle and the advantages your family enjoys.

Maybe HIMS is good for you

I am the first to admit that with, I am told, an ego the size of Manhattan, I am not your average guy. Accordingly, the tenets of AA and TSF are contrary to my personality. But as the author of a book on professional aviation I read many years ago remarked, in order to strap 100 tons of metal to your ass and blast skyward, you *have* to have a bit of an ego.

There are some people well-suited to surrendering control of their lives to HIMS. If that is you, then God bless you and good luck. How many people are thus predisposed is unclear, since HIMS victims quickly become adept at camouflaging their real feelings and motives.

In any case, if you are an otherwise hopeless addict whose wife is moving out and whose house is in foreclosure (or similar disasters befall you), then HIMS might not be just an option, but the *only* way to save your life. *Do not* use this book as an excuse to avoid seeking help.

ADA protections and you

As noted in Chapter 9, even "drunks" (God, I hate that word) are protected by the 1990 "Americans with Disabilities Act" (ADA) ... sometimes. The ADA prohibits discrimination against individuals with disabilities in all areas of public life, including employment.[1] No, it is not a "get-out-of-jail-free" card for showing up drunk to work. You may not violate reasonable work rules. In fact, until you are in recovery, it probably won't help you at all.

Once in recovery, however, you get some protections. Under the ADA, alcohol abusers might be considered disabled if they are alcoholics or recovering alcoholics, particularly if the disease creates an impairment of life activities such as caring for oneself, performing manual tasks, seeing, hearing, eating, sleeping, walking, standing, lifting, speaking, breathing, learning, reading, thinking, communicating, and working. Two federal courts of appeals have ruled that alcoholism meets the definition of a disability.

As a disabled person, employers must allow you certain "accommodations." For example, during a job interview they are not allowed to ask you any questions which might reveal your disability nor, prior to a job offer, can they give you a medical exam whose requirements exceed the requirements of the position – something all major airlines once did. (You can, however, be asked whether you have ever used illegal drugs, or whether you have ever been arrested.)

Other reasonable accommodations might include relief from your work schedule to attend AA or HIMS meetings or therapy, providing such accommodations do not cause your employer unreasonable hardship. However, your employer's patience need not be infinite if, for example, you relapse and require additional residential treatment. Nor are you protected for aberrant behavior, even if you claim it is due to alcohol addiction.

Because only "qualified" employees are protected by the ADA, you might have to prove you are qualified for the essential functions of your job. But if you are performing your job functions as well as other employees, you cannot be unduly disciplined for your disability.

Resources for HIMS victims

The strategy of HIMS bureaucrats is to keep you isolated, fearful, and dependent on them to maintain your career. Like Randle Patrick McMurphy in *One Flew Over the Cuckoo's Nest*, my goal is to demonstrate that you are neither alone nor crazy. I hope your takeaway from this book is that despite what you may be told, you need not be a slave to corporate overseers.

To that end, I have set up resources for you at www.HIMSNightmare.com, where you can find:

- Links to a "HIMS Victims Forum" where you can anonymously compare notes with other unfortunates
- Links to and articles on the Americans with Disabilities Act
- Links to the Equal Employment Opportunity Commission
- Alternatives to Alcoholics Anonymous
- Other resources to help you avoid or, if you must, navigate HIMS

Fixing HIMS

Given the thousands of pilots whose livelihoods depend on HIMS, terminating the program nationwide is clearly not an option. That said, protections for pilots need immediate reform in order to prevent airlines from using HIMS to circumvent work rules.

For starters, airline supervisors who have no qualifications in addiction medicine and too many conflicts of interest have no place in the decision-making process regarding whether a pilot is issued or continues to hold a Special Issuance Medical Certificate (SI). They should be afforded input into the process, of course, but decisions should be limited to substance abuse professionals (SAPs) who "don't have a dog in the fight."

Beyond that, specific limits should be enacted to protect pilots who reject "Twelve-Step Salvation." Rather than branding such people as "dry drunks," HIMS should respect their position and issue an SI to anyone who maintains abstinence.

Given that treatment is based on a disease model, in which genetics and dopamine receptors in the brain are responsible for the physiological basis for addiction, the words "drunk" and "sober" should be excised from the language of SAPs. Calling you a "drunk" implies you are morally and socially reprehensible. Saying you are staying "sober" implies that previously you were perpetually drunk. Neither pejorative expression should play any role in medical treatment.

Help may be on the horizon

With court cases increasingly finding the AA and TSF are indeed religion-based, the days of the FAA relying solely on TSF are numbered. I have spoken to numerous lawyers who are interested in class action litigation to end forced participation in AA.

In Canada, an atheist nurse enrolled in a health care industry counterpart to HIMS recently won a settlement with Vancouver Coastal Health after he was fired for refusing to attend AA. As a result, Vancouver-area health professionals can no longer be required to attend 12-step rehab centers, meetings, or activities. Although the case does not represent legal precedent in the U.S., it does demonstrate the accelerating trend away from religion-based treatment.

Keeping <u>you</u>

The grand irony of HIMS is that you are told you have a disease, but you are treated like a "drunk." And as much as AA stresses "progress, not perfection," in TSF – and particularly in HIMS – you are judged against the desired standard of humility, gratitude and acceptance. Ignoring for a moment that HIMS makes you an indentured servant, what I believe haunts many participants – especially those who kill themselves – is their failure to "change everything" (namely, their entire personality) to comply with the demands of their overseers.

Initially, I tried. I was so committed to the program that my wife even suggested I become a substance abuse therapist after retirement. (Substance abuse professionals everywhere may now thank me for not following that advice.) But I quickly discovered that the more I complied with their demands, the more profoundly depressed and angry I became. Gradually, it dawned on me that AA and HIMS were trying to rip out the personality I had spent nearly six decades working to build – a flawed personality, admittedly, but one with which I am overall quite happy, thanks – and replace it with something that, for me, is an anathema.

The measure of the program is that my overseers didn't really care that I remained abstinent, or that I fully complied with the program requirements; they neither believed nor cared that I didn't even *want* a drink. What they really demanded was my soul, and when I refused to surrender it, the hostility began.

As you may have ascertained, I have an anti-authority streak a mile deep – a trait, I am told, which is common among both alcoholics and pilots. In every file ever kept on me, I am certain it reads, "Does not play well with other children." As such, you might be happier with the terms of the HIMS program than I am. But if you deny those terms exist, you are fooling yourself … another trait, you will hear, common among alcoholics.

But whatever my habits or personality, understand that I have had no significant brushes with the law; am happily married to my soulmate; have two wonderful and successful kids, whose soccer games and concerts I rarely missed, and whom I happily put through college; and I have enjoyed a 35-year airline career utterly free of accidents, incidents and FAA violations.

I made that career possible by adopting a number of operating philosophies, not the least of which is that I don't tolerate incompetence with respect to the conduct of flight. I will be the first to admit that I can, on occasion, be undiplomatic in pointing out such incompetence. But then, I didn't set out to be a diplomat. I set out to be an airline captain, an effort I believe most people I've flown with would judge a success.

By enforcing acceptance and humility, I believe HIMS actively discourages pilots from "making waves" when faced with potentially unsafe conduct by others in the industry. While I initially "drank the Kool-Aid," eventually I began to realize that my earlier approach was the one which truly kept passengers safe.

"Cooperate to graduate"? If you can do it, good for you. Just understand that "cooperate" means either full acceptance or elaborate deception, and that graduation does not truly exist.

As for me, I now reject the forced personality changes demanded by HIMS. I suppose you could say, "Captain Asshole is back."

References:

1. Jennifer L. Mora, "Protecting Alcoholics, Preventing Alcohol Misuse and Distinguishing Between the Two," Insight, March 30, 2016, https://www.littler.com/publication-press/publication/protecting-alcoholics-preventing-alcohol-misuse-and-distinguishing

Appendix A
Glossary of Terms

- **AA:** Alcoholics Anonymous.

- **ADA:** The 1990 "Americans with Disabilities Act," one of America's most comprehensive pieces of civil rights legislation, prohibits discrimination and guarantees that people with disabilities have the same opportunities as everyone else to participate in the mainstream of American life, including employment.

- **AME:** Aviation Medical Examiner, physicians who have undergone training and are FAA-approved to issue pilot medical licenses.

- **BAC:** Blood Alcohol Content, commonly expressed as milligrams of ethanol per deciliter of blood.

- **BOAF:** Birds of a Feather International, a pilots' organization based on the principles of AA.

- **CBA:** Collective bargaining agreement (i.e. union contract).

- **Continuing Care:** Post-residential treatment comprising group therapy, meetings with the AME, individual counseling, family therapy, relapse prevention treatment, and AA/NA.

- **DOT:** US Department of Transportation.

- **Drug Screen:** A variety of testing methods used to identify drug ingestion. Urine screens include tests for multiple classes of drugs, with each class analyzed using a particular "panel." DOT testing utilizes a five-panel test. Abstinence compliance testing is typically a 10 or 12-panel test. Other methods of testing include hair and nail samples. The detection window varies with the drug consumed and method of testing.

- **DUI:** Driving Under the Influence.

- **EtG:** Ethyl glucuronide, a specific direct biomarker of ethanol. EtG urine testing is highly sensitive and may produce false positive results due to incidental alcohol exposure such as through the use of mouthwash, over-the-counter medications, or other consumer products.

- **EtS:** Ethyl sulfate. Recent scientific studies have identified (EtS) as a second specific metabolite or biomarker of ethanol. The detection of EtG and EtS offers greater sensitivity and accuracy for determination of recent ethanol ingestion, than by detection of either biomarker alone.

- **FAA:** Federal Aviation Administration.

- **FAR:** Federal Aviation Regulation.

- **FAR Part 67:** Code of Federal Regulations section dealing with pilot medical certification.

- **GC/MS:** Gas chromatography/mass spectrometry urine test for drug screening.

- **Group Therapy:** Per FAA and HIMS, the term refers to clinical group therapy led by a trained clinician.

- **HIMS:** "Human Intervention Motivation Study," an occupational substance abuse program designed for professional pilots and approved by the FAA.

- **Immunoassay:** A means of urine drug testing which is cheaper and easier than GC/MS. Also known as "point-of-care" or "office collection," immunoassays should be considered only the first step in drug testing because they have a higher rate of diagnostic inaccuracy, including false-positive results.

- **IMS:** Independent Medical Sponsor, AMEs who sponsor pilots for Special Issuance medical certificates.

- **IOP:** Initial Outpatient therapy, completed after inpatient treatment (rehab).

- **Monitoring:** Post-treatment activities directly related to compliance with the requirements of the pilot's HIMS program, including peer meetings, supervisory meetings, and sobriety testing.

- **NA:** Narcotics Anonymous, the drug abusers version of AA.

- **NIAAA:** National Institute for Alcoholism and Alcohol Abuse. This organization provided partial funding for the inception of HIMS.

- **P&P:** Psychological and Psychiatric Evaluation required by FAA for the SI.

- **PEth:** Phosphatidylethanol testing. PEth is a direct biomarker blood test considered an accurate indicator of steady moderate and binge-type consumption. The test, while accurate, is not particularly sensitive to low levels of consumption. It is specific for EtOH, with no known false positives (at least according to its proponents), and increases the detection window up to three weeks and, in some cases, beyond.

- **SAP:** Substance Abuse Professional.

- **SI:** Special Issuance Medical Certificate, FAA medical certificates awarded to airmen who meet special conditions and would otherwise be ineligible for a medical certificate.

- **SIA:** Special Issuance Authorization, a letter received by an airman stipulating the authority to issue, and requirements associated with, a Special Issuance medical certificate.

- **TSF:** "12-step facilitation" therapy, based on AA or similar 12-step programs as originally recommended by the founders of Alcoholics Anonymous.

Appendix B
DSM-5* Criteria for 'Alcohol Use Disorder'

DSM-5 In the past year, have you:	
Had times when you ended up drinking more, or longer, than you intended?	
More than once wanted to cut down or stop drinking, or tried to, but couldn't?	
Spent a lot of time drinking? Or being sick or getting over other aftereffects?	The presence of at least 2 of these symptoms indicates an Alcohol Use Disorder (AUD).
Wanted a drink so badly you couldn't think of anything else? ** This is new to DSM-5**	
Found that drinking – or being sick from drinking – often interfered with taking care of your home or family? Or caused job troubles? Or school problems?	
Continued to drink even though it was causing trouble with your family or friends?	The severity of the AUD is defined as:
Given up or cut back on activities that were important or interesting to you, or gave you pleasure, in order to drink?	Mild: The presence of 2 to 3 symptoms
More than once gotten into situations while or after drinking that increased your chances of getting hurt (such as driving, swimming, using machinery, walking in a dangerous area, or having unsafe sex)?	Moderate: The presence of 4 to 5 symptoms
Continued to drink even though it was making you feel depressed or anxious or adding another health problem? Or after having had a memory blackout?	Severe: The presence of 6 or more symptoms
Had to drink much more than you once did to get the effect you want? Or found that your usual number of drinks had much less effect than before?	
Found that when the effects of alcohol were wearing off, you had withdrawal symptoms such as trouble sleeping, shakiness, restlessness, nausea, sweating, a racing heart or a seizure? Or sensed things that were not there?	

*Diagnostic and Statistical Manual of Mental Disorders (5th ed.; DSM–5; American Psychiatric Association, 2013).

Appendix C
HIMS Certification Process

HIMS Certification Flowchart

Minimum Elapsed Time: 8 months or more

Substance abuse evaluation
(variable time frame)

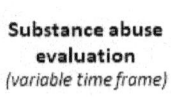

Residential treatment
(min 28 days)

Concurrent
- Intensive Outpatient Therapy *(90 days, variable)*
- 90 AA meetings in 90 days
- Soberlink alcohol monitoring
- Peer monitor/ HIMS meetings

Concurrent
- Group after-care/monitoring *(90 days variable)*
- AA Meetings (3-4 per week)
- Random drug testing (14X annually)
- Peer monitor/ HIMS meetings

Psychological & Psychiatric Exam

Application to FAA

At FAA
- FAA consideration of application *(45-90 days)*
- Special Issuance Authorization (or denial)

Appendix D
HIMS AME Checklist

HIMS AME Checklist - Drug and Alcohol Monitoring Recertification
(Updated 08/30/17)

Airman Name _____ PI# _____

Instructions to the HIMS AME:
- Address the following items based on your in-office exam and documentation review;
- Submit this **Checklist** (it must be signed and dated by the HIMS AME); **AND**
- Include supporting documentation reviewed to complete this checklist (including your HIMS AME report) within 14 days to:

Federal Aviation Administration
Civil Aerospace Medical Institute, Bldg. 13
Aerospace Medical Certification Division, AAM-313
PO Box 25082
Oklahoma City, OK 73125-9867

I reviewed the airman's HIMS Authorization Letter dated: _____
(Date of Authorization letter)

1. **HIMS AME FACE-TO-FACE, IN OFFICE EVALUATION:** Required **EVERY 6 months for ALL CLASSES**
   Any concerns that the airman is not successfully engaged in a continued abstinence-based recovery program or is not working a good program based on your clinical interview/evaluation and review of reports?
   - Interval evaluations (every 3 months or as required by Authorization Letter) were unfavorable?
   - Any evidence or concern the airman has not remained abstinent?
   - Any positive drug or alcohol tests since last HIMS evaluation?
   - Any evidence of noncompliance or concern the airman is not working a good recovery program
   - Any NEW condition(s) that would require Special Issuance? (Do not include any new CACI qualified condition.)

No	Yes

2. **TREATING PSYCHIATRIST REPORT** or **HIMS PSYCHIATRIST REPORT:** Required **EVERY 12 months for ALL CLASSES** unless a different time interval is specifically stated in the Authorization Letter.
   - Report(s) is/are favorable (no anticipated or interim treatment changes)
   - The psychiatrist recommends no additional treatment or monitoring

Not Due	Yes	No

Items 3 - 5: The AME should review. Do not submit these items (3-5) to the FAA unless concerns are noted.

3. **AFTERCARE COUNSELOR REPORTS:** For 1st and 2nd class: Required every 3 months, 3rd class: Per Authorization Letter.
   - Show continued participation and abstinence-based sobriety?

N/A	Yes	No

4. **CHIEF PILOT REPORT(S):** Required monthly for commercial pilots holding first- or second-class certificates (N/A for third-class):
   - Report(s) is/are favorable?

N/A	Yes	No

5. **PEER PILOT REPORTS:** Required monthly for commercial pilots holding first- or second-class certificates (N/A for third-class):
   - Report(s) is/are favorable with continued total abstinence?

N/A	Yes	No

6. **ADDITIONAL REPORTS:** Required **ONLY** when specified by the Authorization letter
   - HIMS related (AA attendance, therapy reports, etc.) are favorable and meet authorization requirements
   - Reports required for other **non-HIMS** conditions all meet Authorization requirements

N/A	Yes	No

7. I have no other concerns about this airman and recommend re-certification for Special Issuance.

Yes	No

_____   _____
HIMS AME Signature   Date of Evaluation

If ALL items fall into the clear column, the AME may issue with the time limitation specified in the Authorization letter.
If ANY SINGLE ITEM falls into the SHADED COLUMN, the AME MUST DEFER or contact the FAA for guidance AND EXPLAIN in the HIMS evaluation report.

Appendix E-1
FAA Special Issuance Authorization (SIA)

Federal Aviation Administration
Civil Aerospace Medical Institute (CAMI)
Aerospace Medical Certification Division

P.O. Box 25082
Oklahoma City, OK 73125-9867
(405) 954-4821

Ref:

Subject: Authorization for Special Issuance of an Airman Medical Certificate

Dear

This Authorization supersedes our previous authorization dated   due to a change in your Independent Medical Sponsor (IMS).

I have reviewed all information available in your agency medical file in support of your request for airman medical certification. The available medical evidence reveals an established medical history and/or clinical diagnosis of: **substance dependence (alcohol)**. The findings are disqualifying for an unrestricted airman medical certificate under Sections 67.107(a)(4), 67.207(a)(4), and 67.307(a)(4) of Title 14, Code of Federal Regulations, (14 CFR) Part 67.

However, based on your current clinical status, I have determined that you may be granted an Authorization for Special Issuance of a **first-class** airman medical certificate under 14 CFR § 67.401. This letter supersedes any prior Authorizations and any previous determination letters of denial, ineligibility or withdrawal of an Authorization.

The enclosed <u>corrected</u> medical certificate expires on
This certificate supersedes any previously issued certificates.

This Authorization expires on

This Authorization **REQUIRES THAT YOU MUST:**

• <u>Comply</u> with all of the following conditions or your Special Issuance will be withdrawn.

• <u>Not change</u> your Independent Medical Sponsor (IMS) without prior FAA approval.

• <u>Present</u> this Authorization letter to your IMS and Aviation Medical Examiner (AME) at each visit.

• <u>Submit</u> the following documentation required under this Authorization directly to your IMS for review **prior to** seeing your AME for issuance of interim certificates or undergoing periodic FAA issuing interim certificates or undergoing periodic FAA medical examinations required by class of certificate:

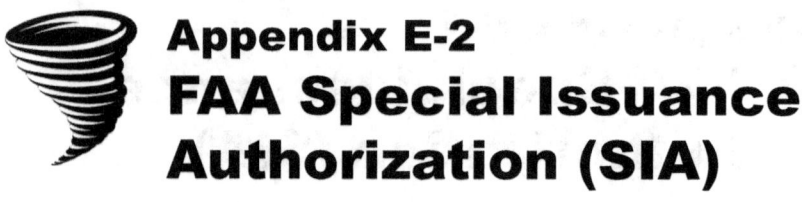

Appendix E-2
FAA Special Issuance Authorization (SIA)

All information at the time intervals specified under **Airman Instructions and Requirements for Continued Special Issuance for Drug and Alcohol Monitoring** (see following pages).

You meet the CACI program criteria for ▓▓▓▓▓▓▓▓▓▓▓▓▓▓ your condition(s) will be monitored by your AME under the CACI program. Prior to your March 2019 FAA medical examination, and every 12 months thereafter, you should follow these steps:

Consult your AME or the online CACI criteria at: www.faa.gov/go/caci to identify the reports and/or testing required by the FAA.

Using the CACI worksheet as a reference, ask your healthcare provider for a current medical summary that addresses the items on the worksheet and include any required testing.

Give the required documentation to your AME at the time of or prior to your FAA medical examination.

If you do NOT provide the required documentation to your AME, or if you are not otherwise qualified, the AME is instructed NOT to issue a certificate. If you continue to meet CACI criteria, your AME will continue to follow this condition.

[Note: Your treating physician/providers may not require the testing or follow-up required by this special issuance for your clinical care, but the FAA requires them to determine whether you may continue to be safely special issued airman medical certificates.]

- If you do NOT provide the required documentation to your IMS and your AME, or if you are not otherwise qualified, the AME must NOT issue a medical certificate.

- If your IMS has given a report to you examining AME indicating that you meet all requirements of this Authorization for re-certification, and if you are otherwise qualified, your HIMS AME is authorized to special issue an airman medical certificate time-limited to **no more than 6 months** for any class of pilot duties.

Appendix E-3
FAA Special Issuance Authorization (SIA)

WARNING(s):

- Your IMS, AME, HIMS/treating psychiatrist or treating physician MUST immediately report to the FAA:

  ANY deterioration in abstinence or recovery (call 405-954-4821);

  ANY new condition that would require special issuance (report in writing).

You are cautioned to abide by Title 14 of the Code of Federal Regulations (CFRs), Section 61.53, relating to physical deficiency. Because of your history of hypertension, asthma, and hypothyroidism, operation of aircraft is prohibited at any time new symptoms or adverse changes occur or if you experience side effects, or require a change in medication and/or treatment.

Continued airman certification remains contingent upon total abstinence from alcohol and mood altering chemicals.

This Authorization will be withdrawn if you do not comply with any of the conditions for continued eligibility of this Authorization.

Appendix E-4
FAA Special Issuance Authorization (SIA)

Airman Instructions and Requirements for Continued Special Issuance for Drug and Alcohol Monitoring

1. You must continue to successfully engage in an abstinence based recovery program as prescribed and monitored by your Independent Medical Sponsor (IMS), and subject to minor modification as deemed necessary to meet your individual needs.

2. **AT LEAST 14 times per 12 month interval**, undergo random, unannounced drug and/or alcohol testing administered either directly by your IMS or coordinated through an independent third-party testing facility. Results must be provided to your HIMS AME, and your HIMS AME has discretion to require supplemental testing.

3. **EVERY 6 months**, you must complete a face-to-face in person evaluation with ▮▮▮▮ as your IMS.
   The IMS must re-evaluate your continued eligibility for special issuance for the conditions specified under this Authorization and submit a completed HIMS AME Checklist - Drug and Alcohol Monitoring Recertification.
   The required components of the Drug and Alcohol Monitoring evaluation can be found on the FAA Certification Aid - Drug and Alcohol Monitoring Recertification at www.faa.gov/go/HIMS-DA.

4. **EVERY 12-months**, you must see Dr. ▮▮▮▮ (your HIMS psychiatrist) to evaluate your overall status and quality of recovery. He/she must submit a clinical report* to your HIMS AME at the time of the evaluation, to include interim documentation when deemed necessary by your HIMS AME.

5. **EVERY-3 months**, provide your IMS with aftercare counselor reports from ▮▮▮▮ attesting to your continued progress and participation in abstinence-based sobriety.

6. **EVERY month when employed**, provide your IMS with reports from ▮▮▮▮ Airlines:
   a. Your chief pilot/flight operation supervisor attesting to your competence, crew interaction, and mood; and
   b. Your HIMS program monitoring representative (e.g., Peer Pilot from your employer, union, etc.) attesting to the best of their knowledge, to your continued total abstinence from alcohol.

7. **When applicable**, reports or information required for any other condition(s) listed in this Authorization.

8. **When applicable**, reports or information required for any CACI conditions.

* Recommendation: give a copy of the "FAA Certification Aid - Drug and Alcohol Monitoring Recertification" at www.faa.gov/go/HIMS-DA to each person providing a report to help ensure that all required information is submitted on your behalf.

Appendix E-5
FAA Special Issuance Authorization (SIA)

Your IMS and (when applicable) your AME should submit all required documentation to the FAA **using only one** of the following addresses:

REGULAR MAIL
Aerospace Medical Certification Division
FAA CAMI, AAM-300
P.O. Box 25082
Oklahoma City, OK 73125-9867

SPECIAL MAIL
Aerospace Medical Certification Division
FAA CAMI, AAM-300
6700 S. MacArthur Blvd., Room 308
Oklahoma City, OK 73169

Modifications of monitoring or medication under this Authorization are at the discretion of the FAA and must be approved in advance. Requests require satisfactory evidence of continued compliance with this Authorization, symptom remission, and favorable recommendations from the IMS, the HIMS/treating psychiatrist, and/or the treating physician.

Sincerely,

 for

David M. O'Brien, MD, MPH
Manager, Aerospace Medical Certification Division
Civil Aerospace Medical Institute

Enclosure: Medical Certificate

cc:

Additional information such as certification Aids, checklists and information on required neuropsychological testing can be found here: www.faa.gov/go/HIMS-DA

Appendix F
Resources

Books

- Lance Dodes, MD and Zachary Dodes, The Sober Truth: Debunking the Bad Science Behind 12-Step Programs and the Rehab Industry, Beacon Press, 2014.
- Joe Miller, US of AA: How the Twelve Steps Hijacked the Science of Alcoholism, Chicago Review Press, 2019.
- Maia Svalavitz, Unbroken Brain: A Revolutionary New Way of Understanding Addiction, Picador, 2016.
- Bill W., Alcoholics Anonymous: The Story of How Many Thousands of Men and Women Have Recovered from Alcoholism, Fourth Edition, Alcoholics Anonymous World Services, Inc., 2001.

Documentaries

- "The Business of Recovery: A Dose of Reality," https://www.thebusinessofrecovery.com/
- "Pleasure Unwoven," https://addictioneducationsociety.org/dr-kevin-mccauley-pleasure-unwoven/
- "The Thirteenth Step," https://www.the13thstepfilm.com/

Online resources

- AA Agnostica: https://aaagnostica.org/
- Alcoholics Anonymous: https://www.aa.org/
- Birds of a Feather International: www.boaf.org/
- Brain HQ: https://www.brainhq.com/
- C3 Foundation: https://cthreefoundation.org/
- Equal Opportunity Employment Commission: https://www.eeoc.gov/

- ❏ FAA, "Alcohol and Flying": www.faa.gov/pilots/safety/pilotsafetybrochures/media/alcohol.pdf
- ❏ HIMS program website: https://himsprogram.com/
- ❏ HIMS resources: www.himsnightmare.com
- ❏ HIMS victims forum: http://hims-victims.freeforums.net/
- ❏ Lumosity: https://www.lumosity.com/
- ❏ SMART Recovery: https://www.smartrecovery.org/

www.ingramcontent.com/pod-product-compliance
Lightning Source LLC
Chambersburg PA
CBHW071853070526
44583CB00016B/1670